D1314752

Financial Analysis and the New Community Development Process

Richard L. Heroux
William A. Wallace

The Praeger Special Studies program—
utilizing the most modern and efficient book
production techniques and a selective
worldwide distribution network—makes
available to the academic, government, and
business communities significant, timely
research in U.S. and international economic, social, and political development.

Financial Analysis and the New Community Development Process

PRAEGER SPECIAL STUDIES IN U.S. ECONOMIC, SOCIAL, AND POLITICAL ISSUES

Praeger Publishers New York Washington London

PRAEGER PUBLISHERS
111 Fourth Avenue, New York, N.Y. 10003, U.S.A.
5, Cromwell Place, London S.W.7, England

Published in the United States of America in 1973
by Praeger Publishers, Inc.

Library of Congress Catalog Card Number: 72-92458

Printed in the United States of America

250672

ACKNOWLEDGMENTS

We appreciate the financial support of the New York State Science and Technology Foundation; the research could not have attained its level of completeness without this grant.

Thanks go to Donald H. Davenport, executive secretary of the Foundation, for his cooperation and encouragement throughout the study.

Page

ACKNOWLEDGMENTS v

LIST OF TABLES AND FIGURES x

Chapter

1 INTRODUCTION 3

   A Review of Financial Planning for New
     Communities 4
   Methodology 4
   Organization of Text 5

2 THE NEED FOR PLANNED COMMUNITIES 7

   New Communities Defined 7
   Scope 9
   Review 9
     Problem 9
     New Communities 10
     The Role of Planned Communities 18
   Summary 20

3 THE NEED FOR FINANCIAL PLANNING MODELS 21

   An Overview 21
     Schema of Decision-Making Process for a
      Planned Community 23
   An Illustration 27
   Concluding Remarks 31

4 A CONCEPTUAL MODEL OF NEW COMMUNITIES 32

   The Problem 32
   The Model 33
     Constraints That Depend on the Planned
      Population of the Development 34

Constraints that Depend on Land Usage   35
Constraints that Depend on the Values of
    the Decision Variables, Number and Type
    of Dwelling   35
Profit Objective   36
An Example   37
Data Requirements   37
Linear Programming Formulation   40
Solution   40
Planned Development and Planned Community:
    A Comparison   52
Conclusions   53
Appendix 4.1—The "Instant City" Model   53
Appendix 4.2—Element Identification   61
Appendix 4.3—Basic Element Cost   62

5   THE LAND DEVELOPMENT PROCESS   67

Market Analysis   68
Population Growth   70
Family Formation   70
Housing Inventory   70
Occupations   71
Income Distribution   71
A Demand Schedule   71
Housing-Related Activities   72
Industry   72
Commercial   73
Educational   73
Service-Oriented Activities   73
Facility-Oriented Activities   74
Land Requirements   74
Residential   74
Industry   75
Commercial   75
Education   76
Service-Oriented Activities   76
Facility-Oriented Activities   76
Land Sale Proceeds   76
Land Value Flow Chart   78
Investments and Costs   80
Land Investment   80
On-Site and Off-Site Improvements   81

Chapter		Page
	Operating Expenses	84
	Housing Construction Costs	84
	Costs Allocation	85
	Financial Analysis	85
	Profit and Loss Statement—No Financing	86
	Cash Flow Statement—No Financing	87
	Profit and Loss Statement—Financing	87
	Cash Flow Statement—Financing	88
	Measures of Performance	88
	Appendix 5.1—Sample Output From Financial Analysis Model	89
6	MULTI-PERIOD MODEL	115
	Constraints That Depend on the Planned Population of the Development	116
	Constraints That Depend on Usage	116
	Constraints That Depend on Land Allocation	118
	Parcelization Constraints	119
	Profit Objective	120
	Revenue Objective	121
	Appendix 6.1—A Detailed Multi-Period Model Description	121
7	THE ROLE OF LINEAR PROGRAMMING IN THE LAND DEVELOPMENT PROCESS	129
	Land Development Process Flow Chart	131
	Blocks 1-5	131
	Blocks 6-10	131
	Blocks 11-16	131
	Blocks 17-18	133
	Blocks 19-21	133
8	LINK ANALYSIS	134
9	AN APPLICATION OF THE MULTI-PERIOD MODEL: A CASE STUDY OF THE HIGHLANDS PROJECT	138
	Iterations of the Linear Programming Model	146
	Iteration 1	146
	Iteration 2	149

Chapter   Page

            Iteration 3   149
            Iteration 4   150
            Iteration 5   150
            Appendix 9.1—Financial Analysis For Case
            Study   155

10   EXTENSIONS TO THE CASE STUDY   159

     Range   159
            The Current Solution   160
     Parametric Programming   160
            A Governmental Request   161
            Sensitivity of Current Solution to Revenue
            Changes   163

11   CONCLUDING REMARKS   165

     Summary and Conclusions   165
     Suggestions for Further Study   166

REFERENCES   169

ABOUT THE AUTHORS   173

LIST OF TABLES AND FIGURES

Table	Page
2. 1 American and European New Communities	8
4. 1 Basic Linear Programming Data	38
4. 2 Postoptimality Data	41
4. 3 Optimal Distribution of Population in Planned Development	42
4. 4 Optimal Land Use Plan for the Planned Development	44
4. 5 Infrastructure Usage as Determined from Optimal Land Use Plan	46
4. 6 Development and Municipal Account Summary	47
9. 1 Regional Housing Projection, 1970-90	139
9. 2 Projected Housing Demand for the Site, by Income, Price or Rent, Tenure, and Number of Bedrooms, 1974-83	141
9. 3 Site Household Characteristics, 1974-83	142
9. 4 Summary Characteristics of the Projected Households	143
9. 5 Projected Demand Schedule, 1974-83	144
9. 6 Land Sale Prices Summary, 1973, 1976, and 1979	147
9. 7 Site Improvement Costs Summary, 1973, 1976, and 1979	148
9. 8 Proposed Parcelization Schedule, 1974-83	152
9. 9 Proposed Development Schedule, by Type of Dwelling Units, 1974-83	153
9. 10 Case Study Data for Link Analysis	154

Figure

3. 1 Decision-Making Process for a Planned Community | 22
5. 1 Financial Analysis Flow Chart | 69
5. 2 Land Value Flow Chart | 79
7. 1 Land Development Process Flow Chart | 132

Financial Analysis and the New Community Development Process

The development of a new community can change the growth patterns of a region, affect the natural environment of many thousands of areas, and absorb immense resources. Columbia, Maryland, changed Howard County into a suburb, is creating an "urban" environment in the midst of farm land, and requires investment monies in the neighborhood of $50 million.

Developers of such communities have had little guidance from tested theories or propositions. European new towns were built in different economic and social environments. Research has been at best cursory, where it has existed. Although the development of Columbia, Maryland, and Reston, Virginia, are providing some information and research is being conducted, a need is still evident for more insight into one of the key problems in using new communities as an instrument for the implementation of a national urban growth policy: financing—the amount and type of the economic resources that must be made available.

Examples abound (and will be discussed in some detail in the text) of developers having financial difficulties in developing new communities. However, clear delineation of what the problems were and what caused them are not available.

Financial failures may be due to any of several reasons: inadequate financial planning, an inflexible plan for development resulting in the inability to vary the methods of financing to meet unrealized needs, or incorrect assumptions employed in the financial analysis. Confounding the financial problem is the lack of a precise definition of the development process for a new community, resulting in the inability to identify the cash inflows and outflows relating to this process. The research to be described herein seeks to delineate the development process, resulting in an explicit identification of the cash inflows and outflows, and proposes a new methodology for arriving at a plan for development. It is hoped that application of the results of the research will achieve the following: (a) decrease the need for potentially prohibitive assumptions in the financial analysis; (b) provide a greater understanding of the chosen plan in terms of alternatives, limitations, and sensitivity to market changes, and (c) yield an optimal plan for which alternative methods of financing may be considered and the best combination chosen.

A REVIEW OF FINANCIAL PLANNING FOR NEW COMMUNITIES

Much of the research currently being conducted on new communities does not explicitly address the problem of financing. Those works found to be relevant deal with (a) the costs of new communities [55,56],* (b) rate of return models for new communities [17,35,51, 65,66], and (c) cash management [57]. Cost studies present detailed accounts of the expenses involved in new community development, showing use and amount of necessary financial outlays. Rate of return models permit the development entity to calculate, given various assumptions of financing costs, its return on investment. Articles dealing with cash management focus on delineating revenue and costs, including the time value of money. More specifically, aggregated cash requirements, which arise from the asynchronization of cash inflows and outflows, are presented in the form of a cash budget for the duration of the project. Thus, the amount and timing of financing needs, as well as forecasted cash inflows and outflows during each period, are specified. However, the problem of how these financing needs are met is not resolved.

Noticeably missing among each of the above is an explicit description of the development process. The plan for development is assumed given; the question of how this plan should be financed is unanswered. Though this question is certainly important and worthy of study, until more work is done little useful research can be accomplished on the nature of financing new communities. This research endeavor addresses this problem and its ramifications.

METHODOLOGY

A review of the literature relevant to the financing of new communities has revealed that there does not currently exist a compact

---

*Figures in bracket indicate sources listed under "References" at end of volume.

body of analytical thought in this field. The only analytical work to
date consists of computer simulations of cash flow. Work conducted
by General Electric/Tempo [19] is the most extensive and does describe the development process to a greater extent than do similar
works [13,51,61]. It is apparent that a simulation does provide a
logical description of this process, but does not yield innovative
insights on the best way of directing the development. Rate of return,
or cash flow analysis, is the accepted mode of analyzing the financial
feasibility of a new community development plan, but it is not appropriate for determining the amount, type, or timing of these financing needs.

ORGANIZATION OF TEXT

Chapter 2 describes and defines new communities. Their
purpose is clarified by categorizing the generic term "new communities" into government communities, planned communities, and
planned developments.

Chapter 3 presents an overview of the decision-making process
for a planned community. In addition to acquainting the reader with
the type of financial problems that arise in the development of new
communities, this chapter is intended to introduce the reader to the
interrelationships among the various components of a new community
development. A specific description of some of these components—
land use plan, financial model, and so forth—is the subject of later
chapters.

Chapter 4 attempts to place this research in its proper perspective. In order to understand the nature of the finance problem
confronting developers, it is necessary to explicitly describe the development process and to have a means of dealing effectively with the
decisions required in this process. An "instant city" conceptualization
for a new community is proposed and is formulated as a single-
period linear programming model. Data are developed, and a solution
is obtained. The merit of this methodology as an aid in understanding
the development process is analyzed. The instant city conceptualization
is intended to provide an argument for use of the proposed methodology—
not only does it provide a means of dealing with such developments
in a structured manner, but it permits an understanding of the
ramifications of the plan proposed for development.

The chapters that follow Chapters 3 and 4 extend and develop
the ideas presented in those two chapters.

In Chapter 5 the land development process for a new community
is described, and the decisions that must be made during this process
are discussed. This chapter reveals the nature of the finance problem,

i.e., the fact that new communities fail financially is not necessarily due to the lack of adequate financial planning—though in many cases this may be true—but because current analyses consider only financial feasibility, when it is necessary to consider in an integrated fashion market, fiscal, and financial feasibility. This is not an oversight; it simply reflects the inadequacy of current analytical techniques—specifically, simulation models.

Chapter 6 presents the development of a multi-period linear programming model that considers the complex interrelationships discussed and described in Chapter 5. In Chapter 7 the role of this model in the land development process is discussed. Key decisions must be made throughout the development process in order to arrive at a plan for development. The purpose of the model is to serve as a tool that is used to generate information on which these decisions may be made. The model is sequential by design and deals explicitly with the interrelationships among market, fiscal, and financial feasibility.

Market and fiscal feasibility are implicit in the use of the linear programming (LP) model, but financial feasibility is not. Similarly, while the financial feasibility or infeasibility of a specified plan for development is a direct result of employing a financial analysis, market and fiscal feasibility are not. Therefore, in Chapter 8 a procedure is proposed that links the plan for development to the financial analysis.

In Chapter 9 the use of the model as an aid in the development process is illustrated, as is the link analysis. The data used in this chapter were generated in a planning study for a new community. In Chapter 10 postoptimality analyses are presented, using the case study data and results.

The purpose of this research was not to find the optimal methods of financing a new community, as previously discussed. The results of this research provide the background and input information, except for sources of financing necessary to determine the best financing package, given the cash budget. The problem is presented in a cash management framework and is briefly discussed in the summary and conclusions. As a result of this research certain areas requiring further study have been recognized. Where possible, suggested approaches worthy of consideration have been proposed. Both are presented in Chapter 11.

The appendixes contain data, explicit descriptions of the models, and computer outputs from the simulation model.

**THE NEED FOR
PLANNED COMMUNITIES**

NEW COMMUNITIES DEFINED

One often reads of "new communities," "satellite new communities," "dormitory communities," "new towns," and "garden cities." Although at one time these names may have been descriptive, today they are not only nondescriptive but are also confusing.

Numerous publications [45] have been written regarding new communities and new towns; however, their content differs little. Each informs us that there are urban problems and then proceeds to tell us how new communities offer potential solutions to these problems. The difficulty is that new communities, new towns, and so forth are very often not defined or, at best, are ill-defined. Therefore, for purposes of this study "new communities" will be used as a generic term meaning "new towns," "satellite communities," "garden cities," "dormitory communities," and the like. New communities are then categorized as being either "government communities," "planned developments," or "planned communities." These terms are defined as follows:

1. "Planned communities" are those designed and built to establish and test hypotheses involving physical and social goals concerned with man's interaction with his environment.
2. "Planned developments" are communities designed and built for economic gain.
3. "Government communities" are those designed and built by public agencies to meet housing needs.

Table 2.1 categorizes twenty-five such communities—American and European. Land acreage, where available, has also been reported.

TABLE 2.1

American and European New Communities

Name	Acres (thousands)	Planned Development	Government Community	Planned Community
Letchworth, England	3.8			X
Welwyn Garden, England	4.3			X
Park Forest, Illinois	–	X		
Cumbernauld, Scotland	4.15		X	X
Tapiola, Finland	.68			
Levittown, New Jersey	–	X		
Reston, Virginia	3.75			X
Columbia, Maryland	14.1			X
Irvine Ranch, California	88.0	X		
Janns/Conejo, California	11.0	X		
Mission Viejo, California	11.0	X		
Valencia, California	4.3	X		
Vallingby, Sweden	–		X	
Litchfield Park, Arizona	13.0	X		X
Radburn, New Jersey	–			
Sunset City, California	–	X		
San Marin, California	–	X		
San Carlos, California	–	X		
Harlow, England	6.4	X		
Clear Lake City, Texas	15.0	X	X	
Foster City, California	2.7	X		
Sun City, Arizona	14.0	X		
El Dorado Hills, California	9.8	X		
Joppatowne, Maryland	1.3	X		
Greenbelt, Maryland	–		X	

SCOPE

The fact that we have urban problems is indisputable. But there exist two schools of thought as to whether or not new communities are the answer to our urgent urban problems. The first and most boisterous contends, in effect, that the new communities of today will be the new cities of the future. The second school of thought contends that the complexity of new communities precludes implementation. Political scientist Charles Linbloom in supporting this philosophy stated:

> Although such an approach (new community) can be described, it cannot be practiced except for relatively simple problems and even then only in somewhat modified form. It assumes intellectual capabilities and sources of information that men simply do not possess and it is even more absurd as an approach to policy when the time and money that can be allocated to a policy problem is limited, as is always the case. [36]

Alternatively, it is argued that present urban problems can be dealt with more effectively through changes in institutions and laws.

REVIEW

In order to determine if planned communities are necessary, we must first consider the nature of our urban problems. Then, it will be necessary to consider how new communities offer possible solutions to these problems.

Problem

Recent urbanization trends include the following: (a) in-migration of poor into ghettos, (b) the out-migration of the affluent into suburbs, (c) extreme congestion in the cities, (d) the decrease of opportunities in the cities, and (e) destruction of natural resources in suburbs, the movement of industry to the suburbs, and urban sprawl. These trends reflect the interaction of the metropolitan area and rural regions. The implication of these trends on metropolitan living was noted by economist Oliver C. Winston:

All of his [population concentration in huge urban centers]
has raised some serious questions not only about the
impact upon the physical needs to be met but about the
kind of society it implies. Is . . . urban agglomeration
likely to offer the kind of physical, social and aesthetic
environment which will stimulate . . . participation in
social, political and intellectual activities? . . . Does
this kind of development offer enough variety and
choice for people of the next two generations? [67]

Urban sprawl involves unplanned movement to the rural areas;
the National Commission on Urban Problems describes the phenomenon
as

. . . the growth of a metropolitan area through the process
of scattered development of miscellaneous types of land
use in isolated locations on the fringe, followed by the
gradual filling-in of the intervening spaces with similar
uses. [59]

The distinguishing characteristics of urban sprawl are the following:
(a) spiraling land cost; (b) costly public facilities; (c) increased cost
of, and inaccessibility to transportation; (d) poor accessibility to
schools and shopping centers; (e) inefficient county government; and
(f) wasted land resources. This form of growth has had the effect of
excluding low-income and minority groups from suburban housing,
while, at the same time, compelling small farmers to migrate to the
cities, thereby adding to the existent crisis in the cities. In an attempt
to cope with these problems, planned developments have been undertaken in the United States. These developments are techniques
attempting

. . . to rationalize and improve our urban environment
through large-scale, planned developments designed to
provide a range of living, working and recreational
opportunities with a meaningful relationship to one
another. [1]

New Communities

Although urban problems are the concern of those who live in
the United States, such problems recognize no boundaries. The new
communities in Europe have been motivated largely for the same
reasons as those in the United States. Consequently, this section will

consider new communities in Europe, as well as those in the United States.

Planned Communities

These communities have thus far been the result of the efforts of individuals—whether they be philanthropic idealists, such as Ebenezer Howard; ideologists, such as Heikki von Hertzen; or individually wealthy men, such as James Rouse and Robert Simon—who possess a sensitivity to the urban ills confronting man.

The introduction of the Garden City concept in 1898 paved the way for the planned communities that were to follow. Howard's concept was, in effect, a two-phased social experiment. The larger being designed to "lead the nation into a juster and better system of land tenure and a better and more commonsense view of how towns should be built . . ." [27], i.e., he proposed the physical form and the social objectives of the Garden City. He also proposed that 6,000 acres of land would be required—1,000 would constitute the city and the remaining 5,000 would be surrounding agricultural land—all to be owned by the municipality. Howard realized that there were both urban and rural problems and that they were not independent of each other. Therefore, the concentric form of Garden City would facilitate the interaction between the urban and rural sectors of Garden City. This interaction, a producer-consumer relationship, was an important feature of the Garden City concept. In addition, the agricultural land surrounding the city was to serve as a permanent greenbelt that would prevent encroachment. Since Garden City was conceived to be of fixed acreage and population (32,000), growth would necessarily have to take place through colonization. In attempting to condense some of these ideas, Howard viewed Garden City as

> . . . designed for healthy living and industry; of a size
> that makes possible a full measure of social life, but not
> larger; surrounded by a rural belt; the whole of the land
> being in public ownership or held in trust for the commu-
> nity. [28]

The second experiment was to analyze how the residents of Garden City adapted to their new environment. This would be determined by the innovative efforts that would be undertaken by the inhabitants for the common good of the municipality. Howard contended that these efforts would not only be carried out by those members possessing pious opinion, but by those possessing an effective belief in the economic, sanitary, and social advantage of common ownership of land [29].

These concepts were subsequently put to the test in the demon-
stration projects of Letchworth (1904) and Welwyn Garden (1919) in
England. Each of these has maintained Howard's essential ideas:
prosperous industries; homes and gardens with ample open space;
spirited communal life, nearly self-contained, protected by an
inviolate agricultural belt; single ownership; earmarking of surplus
revenues for the municipality; and limited profit. Both of these projects were undertaken by private enterprise that depended solely on
private capital, with the exception that they did receive housing
subsidies from the state. After several years each of those towns
eliminated early financial losses and had high land and property values.
Thus, the success of these two projects, founded on the Garden City
concept, paved the way for the ultimate commitment—nearly thirty
years later—of the national government to meet housing needs in
England.

Originally, home building was strictly within the province of a
governmental agency, but, within the past decade, land has been sold
to private builders. Thus, the government has relinquished some
control, thereby allowing private developers and private capital to
significantly contribute to the success of the entire program. This
shift in policy has enabled the public to react in its own interest.

The Garden City concept has not been restricted to England.
Its importance has been emphasized in its worldwide emulation.
Tapiola [62], the best known and most successful of planned communities, had as its objective the creation of a socially and biologically
correct environment. It was designed as a "laboratory experiment"
to demonstrate and test new methods and concepts of development.
Under its director-developer, Heikki von Hertzen, Tapiola has merged
social goals with the development of an aesthetically pleasing environment. Recently, von Hertzen said that

> . . . every new town should be different. But, a number of
> principles should remain the same—the accent on man and
> his family, serving the pedestrian and not the car, serving
> the consumer and not the producer, respect for nature, no
> air pollution, no water pollution. [64]

Tapiola has been built with every consideration given to these goals.

Like Letchworth and Welwyn Garden Tapiola is a private
venture. Von Hertzen founded the National Housing Foundation,
Asuntosaatio—a private, nonprofit organization, which supplied the
original capital for Tapiola. The success of Tapiola lies in the fact
that a structured social and economic mix of population was planned
in advance and the physical plan formed the basis for implementation
of the social program. Financially, Asuntosaatio has recovered its

investment. Socially, its programs, thus far, are successful. Unlike England, there has been no government initiative made to undertake housing the future population of Finland. Instead, the National Housing Foundation has envisioned a regional complex of six other new towns; whether or not these are to be planned communities is unknown.

It is rather ironical that new British towns and new communities in Sweden and Finland may not have been possible had it not been for an American developer—Clarence Stein. He uniquely merged the theories of Clarence Perry, Ebenezer Howard, and his own revolutionary ideas.

Perry theorized that the total community should be planned as a series of separate neighborhood communities and that pedestrian traffic should be separated from automobile traffic by means of pedestrian thoroughfares linked to a common community center. In this manner residents would realize social benefits derived from ease of access to a common meeting place.

Among Stein's contributions were the "superblock," cul-de-sac, and neighborhood clusters. In addition, he rationalized that large-scale financial investments extended over long periods of time would enable a planned community to attain a substantial population, to be democratically administered, and to provide a wide range and high level of municipal services.

These ideas, joined with Howard's concept of preserving open space, were to be tested in America's first planned community—Radburn, New Jersey. Stein, in 1927, through the City Housing Corporation of New York, a nonprofit organization, founded Radburn. Stein contended that the sponsors for Radburn would have to be limited dividend corporations and organs of the government. As it turned out no government backing was ever obtained, and, with the advent of the depression, the developers dreams were never realized. Today, with all of its revolutionary ideas, Radburn, like many of the communities that followed, stands as a middle- and upper-income community.

During the past decade only two planned communities have emerged in the United States—Columbia, Maryland, and Reston, Virginia. James W. Rouse, developer of Columbia, seems to remain unique among current-day developers in his efforts to

> first . . . create a social and physical environment which
> would work for people, nourishing human growth; and
> second, as a venture of private capital, to make a profit
> in the land development and sale. [26]

The objectives of Robert E. Simon, Jr., developer of Reston, are very similar to those for Columbia. Where Columbia is planning to merge good design with social planning, Reston is merging high-quality architectural design with social goals.

Like their contemporaries, both Reston and Columbia are the result of private ventures. Each has obtained a financially strong backer—Reston is backed by Gulf Oil, while Columbia has the backing of Connecticut General Life Insurance Company. Although neither community receives housing subsidies, Reston was recently awarded a $200,000 federal grant to experiment with innovative housing for moderate-income families. Reston has also formed a nonprofit corporation; the manner in which this corporation will be utilized remains to be determined. Both communities are relatively young. Columbia was begun in 1963 and Reston in 1961. Although the success of these planned communities will not be known for some time to come, Simon, due to a tight money market, has lost control of Reston to Gulf Oil Corporation, which is now the main developer.

As a result of the passage of the Urban Development Act of 1970, which renewed and expanded the commitment Congress made to new towns in the Housing Act of 1968, this decade will witness the emergence of several new planned communities [9]. Among them will be Maumelle, Arkansas; Flower Mound New Town, Texas; Park Forest South, Illinois; St. Charles, Maryland; Jonathan, Minnesota; and Cedar-Riverside, Minnesota. The Department of Housing and Urban Development (HUD) loan-guaranteed commitments have as yet to be made to such projects as Riverton, New York, and Soul City, North Carolina (which would represent the first town to be developed by a black entrepreneur—Floyd McKissick).

Government Communities

As in all new communities the initial impetus to build the community stemmed from existent urban problems. Regardless of what motivating factor was predominant, new communities exemplify a common desire to fill a housing need; but this is where the direct similarity ends. In planned communities the developers are motivated to find a socially viable environment in which to build homes. In contrast, agencies responsible for government communities are motivated primarily by a housing shortage. For example, in the United States a government community may be either a World War I-U.S. Shipping Board community, greenbelt community development, power and reclamation project, or an atomic energy town.

WWI-U.S. Shipping Board communities were a direct reaction to war industry housing shortages. These residential communities were a result of federal sponsorship. Legislation was enacted to establish agencies to be responsible for building and maintaining control of the communities and to supply funds for construction. The construction was by private enterprise, relying heavily on the Garden

City principles. Among the accomplishments attributed to these
efforts were the following: (a) establishment of new standards for
housing, (b) incorporation of substantial low- and moderate-income
housing, and (c) introduction of innovative housing. However, cognizance
of the need for continuing community administrative authority and
local government authority was realized. For example, among the
affects poorly planned withdrawal of federal influence had on Noreg
Village, Pennsylvania, were the following: (a) it destroyed the economic
base of the community, (b) it caused reversion of titles on home
mortgages, and (c) it badly scrambled the financial affairs of the
community.

Greenbelt communities were developed because of the need for
housing following the depression. These communities provided only
low-income housing. When the government discontinued financing
these communities, they had to depend on their own resources.
Subsequently, land and home prices soared. Gradually, the low-income
families were phased out; today, Greenbelt, Maryland, one such
community, is a middle- and upper-middle income community. These
endeavors, which resulted in a short-lived commitment to social
objectives, exemplify the shortcomings of direct federal ownership
and operation of communities. Of particular note is the lack of
financial and political involvement of state and local government.

Power and reclamation projects are typified by Boulder City,
Nevada, and Norris, Tennessee. Both communities were federally
sponsored. The disposition of Boulder City met with citizen opposition—
attributed to the failure of the government to prepare adequately for
transfer of control. In contrast, Norris, which was also built to house
workers, illustrates the effects of adequate preparation for transfer
of control, since it is a viable community. Moreover, the smooth
transition of Norris to corporate status preserved the charm of the
Radburn principles followed in its design.

Atomic energy towns, such as Oak Ridge, Tennessee, and Los
Alamos, New Mexico, although federally sponsored, illustrate the
ease with which incorporation may take place if prepared for. During
their early years, prior to incorporation, plans were developed for
incorporation and transfer of authority. In contrast to previous
government communities, adequate provision was made for continual
federal financing aid after federal ownership ceased. The passage of
the Atomic Energy Commission Act of 1955 ended government ownership and control of these communities.

Government communities in Europe differ from those in the
United States. Two kinds exist—those undertaken by the national
government and those undertaken by the municipal government. These
communities have been built because the government displayed fore-
sight in recognizing its need to house its population or because it

assumed responsibility for the same after a planned community had
demonstrated the need for government involvement and the value of
maximizing man's interaction with his environment.

The best example of the latter is England. Government communities in Britain have preserved the essential ideas of Ebenezer
Howard. Harlow, the first post-World War II government community,
comes closest to meeting Howard's ideas. It has the general concentric form of Garden City, with refinements.

The objective of Harlow was to relocate the population and
industry of London in a balanced government community. This community differed from Howard's concept in one important respect—instead
of growing through colonization, as originally hypothesized, it grew
through expansion. Consequently, Harlow has constantly been growing
and adapting throughout its life span.

An example of the second wave of government communities is
Cumbernauld, Scotland. This community is an "autoage" Garden City.
Unlike the concentric physical form it has a linear center, with
vertically segregated vehicular routes and pedestrian areas. Socially,
its objective is to assist in relieving the congestion of Glasgow.

Much of the planning employed in the Mark II communities (e.g.,
Cumbernauld) was drawn from experiences with Mark I communities
(e.g., Harlow). The final wave of government communities—Mark III
communities—are best characterized by suburban Runcorn. The
planning of this community was based on the advancements made in
transportation systems since Mark II communities and on certain
physical forms that were originally employed in Cumbernauld. The
social objective was to relieve the overcrowding in North Merseyside
by building a self-contained government community around the
existing town of Runcorn.

Each of the foregoing communities was government sponsored
through development corporations and the Commission for New Towns;
both were established under a series of New Town acts [44]. As in
federally sponsored communities in the United States, substantial
private capital is invested in these government communities.

Sweden emphasized housing as the critical need, as exemplified
by a recent appraisal of Vallingby:

> Vallingby was designed as an attractive and functional
> environment, its social objectives were directed toward
> matter of fact expansion of Stockholm, rather than the
> creation of a satellite town with expected greater social
> integration. [23]

Swedish communities differ from British communities in that they
are suburbs of a large metropolitan area, such as Stockholm. The new

communities do not include industry, make no pretense of self-containment, and have a high residential density, due to an almost exclusive use of apartments. These communities do employ Garden City concepts, as well as those expounded by Stein—traffic segregation, preservation of the environment, and combating social problems.

Planned Developments

The basic difference between planned developments and planned communities is that the former has as its objective maximization of economic gain. Although planned developments may in some cases be similar to planned communities, it is important to realize that development of land for economic gains will not necessarily ensure the best environment for man—the converse is also true.

Planned developments are, by definition, a venture supported by private funds. Therefore, communities constructed as "company towns" are included in this category, while governmental towns such as those previously discussed (Oak Ridge and Boulder City) are not.

The merchant-builder of planned developments is a unique by-product of World War II. He saw the need for housing and was able to merge land purchase, site improvement, house construction, and merchandising to fill this need for economic gain. Aiding in his efforts was the postwar economic boom, rising incomes, and government aid in the form of Federal Housing Authority (FHA) and GI loans. Thus, a prosperous market was created for these builders. Two products of this era were Park Forest, Illinois, and the Levittowns.

Merchant-builders have also joined with owners of large parcels of land to construct planned developments. The owners realized that their holdings could become a profitable real estate venture. Examples of these types of developments are Irvine Ranch, Janss/Conejo, Mission Viejo, and Valencia.

Corporations in fields unrelated to home building are also involved in constructing planned developments. Their raison d'être is usually due to past acquisition of land for purposes that are no longer appropriate. The corporation then turns to planned development to capitalize on its investment. Goodyear's sponsorship of Litchfield Park is such an example.

Oil industries entered the planned development business as a result of their unique tax status. This status permitted them to invest their excess funds in real estate ventures. For example, Sunset International Petroleum has developed Sunset City, San Marin, and San Carlos, all in California, while Standard Oil of New Jersey has developed Clear Lake City in Texas.

   Joint business-governmental efforts characterize the company towns in America. These towns were characterized by a lack of planning. Little, if any, public benefits resulted from these endeavors. Their only contributions were to reveal the potential for large-scale projects and to demonstrate the need for democratic participation by citizens in planning and administration. Kohler, Wisconsin, and Pullman, Illinois, are examples of communities of this era.

   Real estate communities represented an attempt by private investors to accomplish what company towns failed to do. These communities did succeed in developing a "sense of neighborhood," and they are becoming largely self-governing. But these benefits were obtained at the expense of building exclusively upper-income housing. As a result of the risk associated with the large investments required to build these communities, a mix of social, financial, and ethnic status became unattainable. Consequently, Forest Hills Garden, New York, and Riverside, Illinois, were to stand as demonstrations of the profitable potential of privately sponsored communities, and nothing more.

The Role of Planned Communities

   Edward P. Eichler and Marshall Kaplan echo the views of the proponents of laissez-faire when they state that

   the money and the energy which might be committed to
   expanding opportunity for the poor, the young, the aged,
   and the sick should not be diverted to real estate ventures,
   no matter how noble the motives of their sponsors. [16]

They, like the developers of new communities, had previously sincerely expressed the necessity of governmental aid to developers of new communities. From the previous discussion of new communities in the United States, however, it appears the authors comments are in reference to planned developments and not planned communities. This view is upheld by William Alonso, who attacks the premises on which planned developments are built—housing, efficiency, in-migration, preservation of natural resources, and opportunities—and then goes on to conclude that

   a policy that aims at housing a substantial portion of the
   population makes little sense. But . . . a . . . policy that
   would create new towns to test or exhibit innovations which
   might be adaptable by existing cities [may have a great
   deal to be said for it]. [4]

Clearly, Alonso is not only justifying planned communities but is
justifying aid for these endeavors. A key point has been struck in
Alonso's article—experiments whose findings are to be transferred
to the cities. Therefore, a new dimension to the relevance of planned
communities has been recognized. In order to avoid any potential
confusion, these two objectives of planned communities should be
carefully delineated. One is an experiment performed with the intent
of adapting the findings to the source of our urban problems, i.e., in
the cities. The other is an experiment performed to determine the
most viable social environment for man with the intent that, when large-
scale community building is undertaken, these findings will be an
integral part of the new community. Where the first approach
represents a direct attempt to remedy our urban problems, the latter
is an indirect approach to the same, i.e., arresting current trends.

Alonso's point further validates the necessity of a planned
community. Currently, federal funds are used for such programs as
Urban Renewal and Model Cities. Both are attempts to rectify urban
problems with immediate programs. The success or failure of these
programs is not in question, but these programs do cause hardships
and do nothing to change the environment in which these problems are
perpetuated. Would not federal monies be as justified for a planned
community that could evaluate and analyze innovative ideas in an
environment conducive to experimentation?

Morton J. Schussheim [54] discounts the usefulness of new
communities as a means of solving urban problems as they pertain to
the poor. Among the various reasons given were the following: (a)
fiscal considerations, (b) social status, (c) racial discrimination, and
(d) price. All affect whether or not homes can be built at all for the
poor in new communities. Many observers contend that the plight of
the poor goes beyond housing. Such an advocate is Nathan Glazer,
who favors the private income approach. Testifying before the Douglas
Commission in July 1967, Glazer said:

> I have seen that the normal pattern of emergence from the
> slum has had little to do with housing. . . . our main efforts
> must be in job creation, job training, education and the
> like. [20]

Although commendable, Glazer's solution lacks the ingredient of a
viable social environment. Would not his ideas be more useful if put
to a test in a planned community?

All of these views concern communities—existing or future.
President Kennedy summarized the situation well in his first message
on housing when he said, "Our communities are what we make them."
What better way have we to effect what our communities will be or to

determine how our existing ones should be changed than by means of experimentation.

SUMMARY

Planned communities offer an opportunity to evaluate and analyze innovative ideas pertinent to our urban problems. It has been argued that they represent the only means available to perform experiments in an environment conducive to experimentation. The results of these experiments may subsequently be adopted in large-scale community developments, such as planned developments and government communities, or to existing communities, such as cities. Historically, the former is actually what has been occurring; the latter suggests grounds for experimentation that, as yet, have not been explored.

If our urban problems are to be dealt with effectively, such that our society offers a physical, social, and aesthetic environment to those who desire it, then planned communities must be the predecessors of the communities of the future.

3

THE NEED FOR
FINANCIAL PLANNING
MODELS

AN OVERVIEW

In Chapter 2 it was seen that a planned community is an experiment undertaken

> to identify and evaluate such innovations [social and physical] and to organize a full-scale demonstration, whether of an entire community or selected elements. [14]

Figure 3.1 represents a schema of the decision-making process employed in the development of a planned community. The land development process described in Chapter 5 and illustrated in the land development process flow chart (Figure 7.1) is a detailed extension of the overview herein presented. (Reference to Figure 3.1 should be made throughout this chapter, although the sequence is not distinct).

The developer of a planned community is from the outset faced with a crucial financial decision. The quantity and location of land that will become the community is known, but the amount and timing of needed finances for this purchase, though crucial, is seldom well planned. Either prior to, or during, land purchases, a long-term loan is obtained. This loan plus personal equity is what is commonly referred to as "front money." It is not uncommon for developers to expect this capital to last until the building of the community is begun. Therefore, until the developer has finalized his land use plan (block 14), it is not unrealistic to assume he has a fixed budget.

FIGURE 3.1

Decision-Making Process for a Planned Community

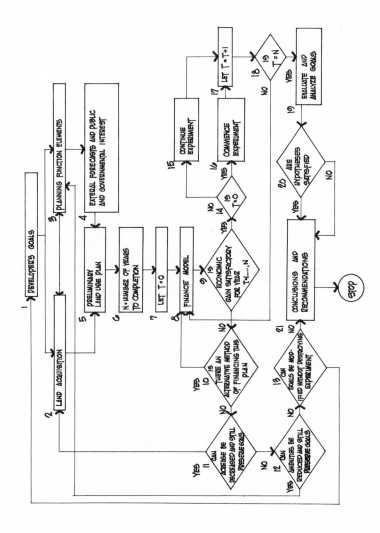

Schema of Decision-Making Process for
a Planned Community

Block 1

Prior to a decision to acquire land, a developer will express
in general terms the purpose of the community. For example, it may
be proposed that "the new community will consist of a population
composed of ethnic mixes in a viable environment."

Block 2

In a planned community land would be purchased in small parcels,
involving many transactions, over a period that could easily exceed
one year. Two exceptions arise if (a) the developer already owns the
land, or (b) the land is purchased from a few large landowners. Among
the options available for purchase are the following: (a) to pay cash,
or (b) to make a modest down payment, with the remainder subject to
a delayed settlement date with a fixed interest charge. Due to the
unplanned nature of these acquisitions, several problems may arise.

1. If too much cash is used for the purchases, a defi-
ciency in capital may result for land development and
for meeting the necessary carrying costs that arise for
property taxes on the land held.
2. If purchase terms are such that payments are delayed, then the developer faces the risk of being bur-
dened with debt when capital is required for additional
land purchases or land development and construction.
3. If acquiring title to the land desired is unduly delayed, the developer faces the prospect of requiring
additional loans due to the imminence of the maturity
date on the original loan, purchase settlements, property taxes, and interest charges.

Block 3

The next phase of the planning process is that of land development and construction, all of whose elements—off- and on-site
improvements, wholesaling of improved building lots, housing design
and engineering, and physical construction and retailing—are determined by the planning function. The capital remaining for these

elements is dependent on the planning exercised during land acquisition.
The demise besetting current-day developers is not new. Sir Frederick
J. Osborn exemplified the need for financial planning when discussing
one of the first planned communities, Welwyn Garden City:

> Land alone had cost over 100,000, the share capital avail-
> able for roads, public services, and building was a minus
> quantity, and even with bank overdrafts and mortgage
> loans up to the hilt [land] development was always handi-
> capped by shortage of capital. [49]

The manner in which planning function elements are financed (discussed in blocks 8 and 9 is crucial, since they not only represent the
major cash outflows but set the pattern for future cash inflows.
    The function of planning is twofold: (a) to formulate specific
social and physical goals from those generalized by the developer
(block 1, and (b) to plan the staged development of the planned community. It has been seen (Chapter 2) that the goals are implemented
by the physical form the community will take. Likewise, the latter
determines when funds are used.

Block 4

    Where the planning function determines for what and when funds
will be required (cash outflows), cash inflows are determined on the
basis of the method of financing (see blocks 8 and 9) and reaction to
the planned community in terms of residential, commercial, and
industrial sales. These factors are estimated in advance from forecasts, interviews, and projections.
    In order for the developer to implement the physical form the
community will take, it is necessary that he begin early to solicit
approval for flexibility with respect to zoning ordinances, subdivision
regulations, and building regulations. Similarly, it is important that
he begin early to communicate the objectives of the planned community, not only to avoid public resistance, but to ultimately improve
sales in the community.

Blocks 5-7

    The land use plan, therefore, can be seen to be a well-laid out
plan of what will be built (amenities; residential, commercial, and
industrial units; roads; utilities; and so forth), the number to be built,
and when they will be built. Since these spatial-temporal relationships

will not necessarily be complemented by forecasts and progress made
with public and governmental parties, it is extremely important that
the land use plan be as flexible as possible.

Blocks 8 and 9

      Among the questions left unanswered are who will finance the
elements of the planning function and how will they be financed. The
former will determine the amount of funds required, whereas the
latter determines the source of funds. For example, it is not uncommon for a developer to obtain flexibility in zoning and subdivision
regulations at the expense of financing major off-site improvements,
such as water and sewers. Nor is it uncommon for a developer to
perform major on-site improvements as part of the development
phases. Either one of these expenses would represent a substantial
drain on the budget. Alternatively, developers have created special
districts to finance off- and on-site improvements, thus relieving
them of the burden completely. Yet another alternative employed is
to have a clause in the original loan that provides for subordination
of the loan to a loan for improvement financing. The same type of
argument is true for the other elements. In the case of construction
the developer can either build himself or subcontract to a professional
builder. If he chooses the latter, two equally undesirable situations
exist: (a) he may make a loan to the builder in order to speed up the
development pace so that the cash inflows are appreciated sooner,
or (b) the builder may have to find his own source of financing. In
the latter case the developer is paying property taxes, interest, and
amortization payments while the builder is looking for a source of
funds. The former case is no better; chances are he cannot make a
loan without taking out another loan himself, since, thus far, he has
had only outlays and has not as yet built a single home.
      In order to determine the developer's economic gain, using the
proposed land-use plan, it is not only necessary to first determine
the how and who of financing, which are cash outflows, but cash inflows
must also be determined.
      The complexity arising from various methods of financing, tax
implications, and possible delays that will affect when funds will be
used, which, in turn, may affect the source and amount, simply cannot
be handled without a financial model designed to consider such
complexities.
      The financial failure of Joppatowne, Maryland, is a classic
account of where, had such a financial model existed, it might have
saved an otherwise successful community from bankruptcy. Although
Leon Panitz, the developer, had many financial problems he was

unable to cope with, he recalled in an interview that, if you begin with inadequate front money, "chances are you will borrow too much too soon."

Given another chance, Panitz recalled, "I would allow more for planning and land development. . . . You have to allow for the unexpected" [60].

The absence of a financial plan for dealing with the complexities that arise during the development of a planned community was recently expressed by W. Alonso in the following manner:

> [a] heavy front-end investment . . . presents critical cash flow problems for the private developer . . . a slow down [in development] would be disastrous for him. [5]

It can be seen from this discussion that the land use plan must not only be flexible for the reasons previously mentioned but it must also be adaptable to financial considerations.

Blocks 10-13

If the land use plan is flexible and the economic gain is judged to be unsatisfactory by the developer, then either the method of financing or the land use plan may be modified until an economic gain is obtained that is judged satisfactory. Otherwise, it is known that a planned community with goals as specified is infeasible.

Although the finance model considers alternative methods of financing and chooses the best among them, block 10 permits incorporation of new or possibly overlooked methods of finance into the model.

Blocks 14-18

Until this time the decision-making process was concerned exclusively with planning. Beginning with block 14 the project is begun. The schedule, source of funds, cash inflows, and cash outflows are fixed. But as the development progresses, unavoidable delays may occur that will invalidate the plan. Since the effects of deviating from the plan may be difficult to appreciate, block 17 serves as mechanism for reevaluating the acceptability of the developer's economic gain periodically (monthly or yearly) throughout the life of the project (block 18). Due to the fact that the finance model is designed to consider the financial complexities that may arise (e.g., rate of absorption falls below expectations), an unacceptable economic gain to the developer at any time, t, is recognized and can be compensated for by modifying either the method of finance or the land use plan.

<u>Blocks 19-21</u>

The final success of a planned community is not only measured by a satisfactory economic gain to the developer but ultimately depends on a favorable reaction of the residents to the social and physical innovations that are part of their human environment.

Social research in the planned community may either begin during the building process or when the community has been completed. The research aspect is generally performed through personal interviews or questionnaires. Among the questions that must be answered are the following:

1. Reaction of the residents to the physical design
2. Adaptability of the residents to their new environment
3. Effect of neighborhood planning, i.e., who residents socialized with and the degree of socialization
4. If the community was originally balanced (age structure, income, and so forth), and has it remained so?

The scope of research that must be performed is vast, as noted by Herbert J. Gans [18]. However, the purpose of this thesis is not to evaluate and analyze goals; therefore, this aspect of a planned community will not be considered.

AN ILLUSTRATION

The decision-making process employed in developing planned communities such as Columbia and Reston is not widely known. But in <u>The Community Builders</u> [15], Edward P. Eichler and Marshall Kaplan discuss decisions made prior to the actual building of Columbia (block 16 in Figure 3.1). The decisions leading to Columbia will be summarized, using the block notation of Figure 3.1.

(1) Basically, the goals established by Rouse were to create a better environment, where the land acreage required to meet goals would be small enough to permit personal contact and participation, yet large enough so that little or no state or federal aid would be required.

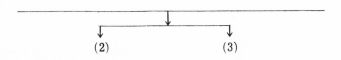

(2)   (3)

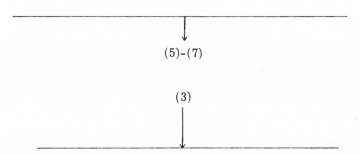

(2)

(2) Approximately 15,000 acres of land were purchased
    in small parcel transactions during a one and one-
    half-year period. Various purchase terms were
    used originally. As purchases were increased new
    sources of capital were required to meet settlement
    dates, mortgage payments on earlier acquisitions,
    funds for overhead, and funds for additional land
    purchases. The source employed would have to
    provide reasonable interest cost, sufficient time
    for repayment, and could not prejudice corporate
    efforts to secure later development funds. Ulti-
    mately, financially strong Connecticut General Life
    Insurance Company was obtained as a backer.

(5)-(7)

(3)

(3) A work group was formed that was responsible for
    determining the social objectives of Columbia. In
    formulating community goals economics, political
    and marketing constraints, were to be ignored (block
    4). Among the factors considered that would promote
    social interaction were minibus systems for trans-
    portation, bridal paths, "mom and pop" village stores,
    homogeneity among residents of a block, small
    neighborhoods, low density, and ample open spaces.

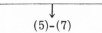

(5)-(7)

(5)-(7) A rough plan was sketched and a twelve-year project duration was estimated.

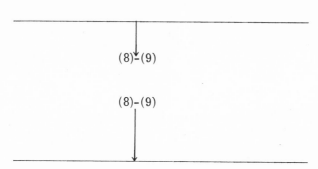

(8)-(9) An economic analysis based on major market
studies, assumptions of densities, land prices,
land allocation, projected population for the area,
number of units, development schedule, absorption rate (units per year), and preliminary estimates of cost from consultants dealing with infrastructure resulted in an unsatisfactory economic
gain.

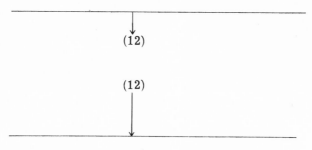

(3) Their analysis revealed it would be more real-
istic to build 25,600 units over fifteen years instead of 30,000 units over twelve years.

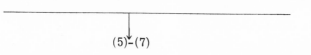

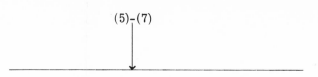

(8)-(9) Further analysis based on additional outlays and
projected cash inflows based on the land use plan
resulted in an unsatisfactory economic gain.

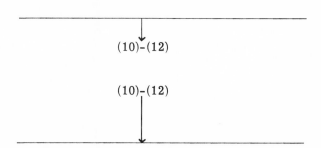

(2)-(7) In an attempt to decrease cost, revisions were
considered with respect to the number of acres of
open space, increasing density, accelerating development pace, reducing developer involvement
through formation of special districts, and reevaluating acreage devoted to industry. Finally, a
decision was reached, based on political considerations. The decision was made to plan only
for contiguous property owned by Rouse. The
effects were to decrease acreage from 15,000 to
11,700 acres; convert open space to industrial
and commercial use; and increase housing density.

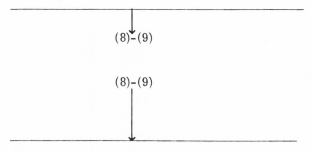

(8)-(9) Although not reported in so many words, it would
appear the economic gain resulting from this

change was satisfactory, since the plan has been
submitted and approved by the county. Therefore, the present plan and marketing strategies
serve as the projections under which actual
development will take place.

CONCLUDING REMARKS

The need for financial planning models is more important than
ever. Recently, J. G. Gliege, discussing new communities, reported
that

it is a wonder that any . . . have survived. In reality they
are barely surviving . . . they are on the brink of fiscal
failure . . . so far in debt they may never be able to pull
into the black again. [22]

A similar account was reported in Urban and Rural America:
Policies for Future Growth, where the Advisory Commission on
Intergovernmental Relations contended that the

infeasibility of [new communities] stems from the investment cost, resulting from the long period required for
land assembly and improvement, and construction of
utilities before revenue from the sale of sites or struc-
tures is sufficient to provide a net profit. [2]

It is important to realize that, even though the finance model
allows the decision maker to consider the financial complexities
associated with the development of a planned community, no remedial
action will be possible unless the land use plan is flexible.

4

A CONCEPTUAL MODEL
OF NEW COMMUNITIES

In Chapter 2 the need for planned communities was thoroughly discussed. Therein, new communities were categorized as being either "government communities," "planned developments," or "planned communities," and these, in turn, were defined.

The purpose of this chapter is to focus on planned communities and planned developments and their interrelationships.

THE PROBLEM

Although the foregoing definitions did clarify the notion of a new community, greater understanding of the relationships between a planned community and a planned development is necessary. Of particular concern is the value of these definitions in providing guidance in studying operational problems.

The need still exists for a way to integrate the various possible land uses into a single land use plan. Current procedures used by the developer are basically "cut and dry," until the best (i.e., most profitable) plan is found. However, this method may not find the most profitable plan and cannot tell the developer what standards are constraining the development.

One problem is the specification of an objective for constructing either a planned community or a planned development. For the latter it is clearly a measure of economic gain, e.g., average rate of return. However, the objective for a planned community is much more nebulous and represents some measure of social welfare. This measure, perhaps a social welfare function, must take into account the cost and benefits of social and physical experimentation.

A study by the Israel Institute of Urban Studies [32] attempts to resolve this problem by the development of a social welfare function.

In that study the objective is the development of a land use plan for a community that satisfies existing constraints, such as the physical environment, economic factors, and so forth, and maximizes "the value of an accepted social welfare function" [32, p. 2]. This is accomplished by assigning monetary values where possible; utilizing linear programming to find a set of suboptimal land use plans based upon the amount of acreage set aside for social services, such as utilities; and then letting the public in the form of their elected representatives make the final choice, i.e., select the "optimal" plan.

This approach does increase the amount of objective analysis. However, the formulation of the social welfare function is still the result of a bargaining process among various competing interest groups, either through established institutions or issue-oriented citizen groups.

The approach taken herein is to use linear programming to find the optimal land use for a planned development, i.e., a community constructed for economic gain; then, by using duality theory, to investigate the relationship between a planned development and a planned community, i.e., one constructed for social benefit. The purpose of solving the primal problem of the linear programming formulation is not in the ultima to determine the precise values of the decision variables, but rather to evaluate the effect of the social constraints imposed on the planned development. It can then be shown that, as the level of physical amenities and welfare attributes— characteristics of planned communities—are increased, the measure of economic gain of the planned development decreases. Therefore, a planned community and a planned development are, in reality, extreme points on a continuum.

THE MODEL

The type of community that evolves from development is dependent upon the nature of the constraints imposed, voluntarily or otherwise, during the development process. These constraints brought about by market forces, zoning, and the like, coupled with the developer's plan for the site, will result in the various land uses, such as residential, commercial, educational, recreational, and so forth, which give the new community its character. The interrelationships among these various land uses may not be known temporally, but can be conceptualized for an "instant city"—a planned development at the horizon. Using this conceptual approach a model is structured so that the complexities arising from the interrelatedness of the various elements of a planned development are accounted for and relatable to those of a planned community.

From a market study the developer is able to determine the demand (X_i) for different dwelling types (i). Lot sizes (j) are then specified for each dwelling type. For nonsingle family dwellings it is necessary to know the number of living accommodations or units (u_{ij}) in each dwelling-lot size combination.

The total population in the planned development at the horizon is a function of the number of people (O_{ij}) residing in each dwelling type (X_{ij}) and can be expressed in terms of the total number of units (Y). Since the various elements in the planned development are interrelated, the number of school children, laborers, and so forth must be some proportion of the total population.

The type of social and physical environment for the community depends upon the portion of the regional market the developer intends to capture with its concomitant supporting facilities. This market strategy also dictates the land resources required to maintain that environment.

The various constraints that characterize a planned development will now be described. The corresponding mathematical description of these constraints are presented in Appendix 4.1.

Constraints That Depend on the Planned
Population of the Development

From the market analysis the projected demand for various dwelling types can be identified. Once the lot sizes for each dwelling type have been determined and the average number of people residing on each dwelling type estimated, the demand for housing can be represented as

$$(4.1) \quad \sum_{j} O(i) . X_{i,j} \leq P(X)_i,$$

where the number of people per dwelling, $O(i)$, is a function of the type dwelling; and $P(X)_i$ is the population projected for each dwelling type.

Two constraints that may be binding on the population if not properly planned for are those for employment opportunities:

$$(4.2) \quad P(t) \cdot Y \leq E(t),$$

where the number of residents per unit employable in a particular industry, $P(t)$, is dependent on that industry; and $E(t)$ is the number of employment opportunities available in each industry; and educational opportunities

$$(4.3) \quad r(K) \cdot Y \leq P(K),$$

where the number of students per unit eligible for each type of school is $r(K)$; and $P(K)$ is the number of students planned for the Kth-type school.

Constraints That Depend on Land Usage

The land that will be required for residential development will depend on the lot sizes used and is given by

$$(4.4) \quad \sum_j a(j) \cdot X_{i,j} \leq \alpha(i) \cdot A,$$

where the land used for each dwelling, $a(j)$, is a function of the lot size; $\alpha(i)$ is the proportion of the land available for development, A, which is made available for each dwelling type i.

Other land requirements are dependent on the total population and the per capita acreage requirements characteristic to each of the uses. Among the land uses that may be considered in a planned development are the following:

(4.5) $a(t) \cdot Y \leq \alpha(t) \cdot A$, for industry;
(4.6) $a(K) \cdot Y \leq \alpha(K) \cdot A$, for educational institutions;
(4.7) $a(c) \cdot Y \leq \alpha(c) \cdot A$, for commercial establishments;
(4.8) $a(P) \cdot Y \leq \alpha(P) \cdot A$, for public services;
(4.9) $a(H) \cdot Y \leq \alpha(H) \cdot A$, for health facilities;
(4.10) $a(F) \cdot Y \leq \alpha(F) \cdot A$, for recreational facilities;
(4.11) $a(\lambda) \cdot Y \leq \alpha(\lambda) \cdot A$, for cultural facilities;
(4.12) $a(g) \cdot Y \leq \alpha(g) \cdot A$, for cemetery use;
(4.13) $a(m) \cdot Y \leq \alpha(m) \cdot A$, for churches.
(4.14) $\sum_i \alpha(i) + \sum_t \alpha(t) + \sum_K \alpha(K) + \sum_c \alpha(c) + \sum_P \alpha(P)$

$$+ \sum_H \alpha(H) + \sum_F \alpha(F) + \sum_\lambda \alpha(\lambda) + \sum_g \alpha(g) + \sum_m \alpha(m) = 1.$$

This constraint allows the developer to determine the value of land over various uses to both himself and to the potential residents. In addition, it allows output of the proportion of land (A) absorbed over the various uses. Finally, it offers a mechanism for controlling land use by constraining or bounding any one or all of these decision variables.

Constraints That Depend on the Values of the
Decision Variables, Number and
Type of Dwelling

It may be noted that several infrastructure elements of the planned development are missing, notably transportation, utilities,

and open space. In this formulation it is assumed that the land
allocated to roads is a fixed multiple, σ, of the land used for all other
elements, (4.4)-(4.13)—the transportation constraints are therefore
redundant. Also, the land used for a sewage treatment plant, a_1, and
a reservoir, a_2, are known and constant. For example, the constraint
for the housing element is given in Appendix 4.1.

Utilities, on the other hand, consume no additional land, for it
is assumed they follow the roads. Consequently, utility constraints,
which are expressed in feet, would be identical to the transportation
constraints saved for a factor τ', which converts miles to feet. Therefore, these constraints are redundant as well.

Open space is assumed to be that portion of the total available
land, TA, not assigned to a land use. Since it is common to devote a
minimum of θ percent of the total available land to open space, the land
that will actually be devoted to open space will be greater than or
equal to θ (TA). This is based upon the assumptions that (a) the total
land purchased, TA, must be used, and (b) land unused for its intended
purpose must be devoted to open space.

Profit Objective

To determine the profit derived from development, it is necessary
to be able to identify or estimate the unit costs and revenues associated with each element in the development. The profit corresponding
to constraints (4.1)-(4.13) is

$$Z' = \Sigma P_{i,j} X_{i,j} + \Sigma R' .a(K)Y + \ldots + \Sigma R' .a(m)Y,$$

where $P_{i,j}$ is expressed in dollars per unit; $P_{i,j}X_{i,j}$ is the profit
derived from the sale of dwellings; and R' is expressed in dollars per
acre, whose value depends on the land use and, when multiplied by the
appropriate housing-related land use, gives the profit derived from
the sale of each type of structure.

One way to determine the total profit to the developer is to
deduct from Z' those "fixed" costs that depend on the land use plan—
namely, the cost of roads, utilities, a reservoir, a sewage treatment
plant, and open space—as well as the total cost of financing. For the
purpose of exposition all investments other than the transportation
systems and utilities will be identified on the "development account,"
with the remaining on the "municipal account."

The model as presented is amenable to solution by linear programming and is described in Appendix 4.1. The application of linear
programming depends on the validity of the assumptions of (a)

proportionality: this implies that the objective function and the constraints are linear, requiring, in turn, that the profit coefficients and the activity coefficients remain constant irrespective of the level of activity; (b) additivity: this requires, for example, that the profit derived from the sales of two dwellings simultaneously is the sum of the profit that would be obtained by marketing each dwelling individually—also, unused resources may not be used to decrease the requirements for other land uses; (c) divisibility: fractional values of the decision variables may be obtained in the solution; and (d) deterministic: this assumption states that all the coefficients in the model are known and constant.

Each of these assumptions can be modified and other techniques of mathematical programming employed (with varying degrees of success). Since the purpose of this model is to explore the interrelationships among the various components of a planned development and to show its relationship to a planned community, the advantages of having existing computational routines permitting feedback and interaction with the model, as well as the insights to be gained from utilizing duality theory, make linear programming the most applicable methodology.

AN EXAMPLE

To illustrate the applicability of the methodology, an example of a planned development for 100,000 people is presented. It is assumed that this development will be within the economic sphere of a metropolitan area; therefore, it need not be completely self-contained. Further, it is assumed that (a) the developer is also the builder and retails all property; (b) elements characteristically rented (shopping centers, apartments, and so forth) are sold; (c) a commitment by public officials to provide services, such as health clinics, a hospital, fire and police protection, as well as a reservoir and a sewage treatment plant, is made to emphasize the sincerity of the endeavor, as well as to improve changes of the ultimate approval of the land use plan; (d) the developer believes that to improve the marketability of saleable property within his development, it is necessary to provide churches, recreational areas, public parks, schools, cultural facilities, cemeteries, and open space.

Data Requirements

The information for this example is based on studies by the Rouse Company [57], Kenneth Wren [68], and P. A. Stone [55]. In

TABLE 4.1

Basic Linear Programming Data

Constraints	Range*		Parameters			Unit Profits			Limits	
Housing	$i = 1$	$j = 1$	$a^d_{ij} = .137$	$Q_{ij} = 3.6$	$P^d_{ij} = 3000$	$u_{ij} = 1$		$\alpha_1 A$	$P^d_i = 69560$	
		$= 2$	$= .171$	$= 3.6$	$= 3310$	$= 1$				
		$= 3$	$= .206$	$= 3.6$	$= 3810$	$= 1$				
	$= 2$	$= 1$	$= .400$	$= 50.4$	$= 2200$	$= 14$		$\alpha_2 A$	$= 15220$	
		$= 2$	$= .562$	$= 50.4$	$= 2600$	$= 14$				
		$= 3$	$= .720$	$= 50.4$	$= 2940$	$= 14$				
	$= 3$	$= 1$	$= .046$	$= 18.0$	$= 1800$	$= 5$		$\alpha_3 A$	$= 15220$	
		$= 2$	$= .069$	$= 18.0$	$= 2000$	$= 5$				
		$= 3$	$= .092$	$= 18.0$	$= 2300$	$= 5$				
Industry	$t = 4$		$P^Q_t = .216$	$(a^m_t)^{-1} = 16$		$c^m_t = 365{,}000$		$\alpha_4 A$	$E = 40000$	
									$M = 20000$	
									$\alpha_t = .30$	
Schools	$K = 5$		$r^s_K = .6$	$a^s_K = 9.5$		$n^s_K = 600$		$\alpha_5 A$	$P^s_K = 16800$	
	$= 6$		$= .46$	$= 30$		$= 1740$		$\alpha_6 A$	$K = 12880$	
	$= 7$		$= .07$	$= 100$		$= 1800$		$\alpha_7 A$	$= 1800$	
Commercial	$c = 8$		$a^A_c = \dfrac{4}{1000}$	$L_c = .8\, P' = 3.6$		$Y_c = 16$		$\alpha_8 A$	$P^A_c = 301{,}000$	
	$= 9$		$= \dfrac{3.75}{1000}$	$= .2 = 3.6$	$\gamma = 4:1$	$= 15$		$\alpha_9 A$	$= 472{,}000$	

38

Constraints	Range*	Parameters		Unit Profits		Limits
Public Services	$P = 10$	$z_P^B = \frac{.13}{1000}$	$a_P^B = 1.5$	$P' = 3.6$	$-c_P^B = 104,000$	$\alpha_{10}A$
	$= 11$	$= \frac{.04}{1000}$	$= 5.0$	$= 3.6$	$= 6,500$	$\alpha_{11}A$
Health Services	$H = 12$	$a_H^L = 1$	$n_H^L = \frac{1}{10,000}$	$P' = 3.6$	$-c_H^L = 1,984,000$	$\alpha_{12}A$
	$= 13$	$= 40$	$= \frac{.1}{10,000}$	$= 3.6$	$= 400,000$	$\alpha_{13}A$
Public Parks and Recreational Areas	$F = 14$	$a_F^R = .5/1000$		$P' = 3.6$	$c_F^R = 10,000$	$\alpha_{14}A$
	$= 15$	$= 1.5/1000$		$= 3.6$	$= 10,000$	$\alpha_{15}A$
	$= 16$	$= 2.0/1000$		$= 3.6$	$= 10,000$	$\alpha_{16}A$
	$= 17$	$= 1.5/1000$		$= 3.6$	$= 10,000$	$\alpha_{17}A$
	$= 18$	$= 3.5/1000$		$= 3.6$	$= 10,000$	$\alpha_{18}A$
Cultural Facilities	$\lambda = 19$	$a_\lambda^c = 2.4$	$n_\lambda^c = \frac{.01}{1000}$	$P' = 3.6$	$-c_\lambda^c = 1,750,000$	$\alpha_{19}A$
	$= 20$	$= 1.38$	$= \frac{105}{1000}$	$= 3.6$	$= 4,020,000$	$\alpha_{20}A$
Cemeteries	$g = 21$		$a_g' = \frac{.26}{1000}$	$P' = 3.6$	$-c_g' = 4000$	$\alpha_{21}A$
Churches and Houses of Worship	$m = 22$	$a_m^H = 2.06$	$n_m^H = \frac{1}{1500}$	$P' = 3.6$	$-p_m^H = 1,449,500$	$\alpha_{22}A$
		$\phi = .60$				

*The subscripts i and j are exactly the same for all other elements as for housing.

39

addition, interviews were conducted with representatives of the New
York State Office of Planning Coordination and the Urban Development
Corporation. Appendix 4.2 identifies the range of values assumed in
the example; basic cost figures corresponding to the range for each
element of the land use plan are given in Appendix 4.3. Data for the
constraints previously developed (pp. 33-37) are represented in
Table 4.1.

In the example employed herein, it is assumed that (a) of the
11,147 acres of total available land, no more than 20 percent is to be
devoted to transportation; in other words, this constraint will not be
violated if the land used for roads is equal in value to 38.6 percent,
σ, of all other land uses; (b) the minimum acreage to be devoted to
open space is ι 28.2 percent of the total available land, i.e., Θ(TA),
therefore, the land to be considered in the model will be A=TA-(.2TA
+Θ(TA) + a_1+a_2), or 5763.3 acres; (c) the municipality will incur
the full expense associated with roads and utilities—while the former
assumption differs somewhat from common practice, the latter is
reasonable, since some utilities with their rate structure are tradi-
tional assets; and (d) the cost of financing will be 6 percent of all
investments in the "development account."

Linear Programming Formulation

The structure of the model has previously been discussed; the
technical coefficients are derived from the parameters; the profit
coefficients from the unit profits (the manner in which unit profits
are calculated and the availability of resources from the limits are
discussed in Chapters 5 and 6). The unit profits and parameters
necessary to form the coefficients and subsequently to determine the
total profit to the developer are summarized in Table 4.2. The notation in each of the tables corresponds to that in Appendix 4.1.

Solution

The dimension of this problem is 29 (constraints) x 31 (decision
variables). It is to be noted that of the 4 constraints represented by
inequalities (4.2) and (4.3), all but 1 are secondary constraints. That
is, in arriving at a solution, only 1 independent inequality in (4.3)
existed. This reduced problem (26 x 31) was solved in less than one
minute, using the MPS/360 package on IBM's 360/50 computer. The
MPS/360 program employs a modification of the revised simplex
method in arriving at a solution.

TABLE 4.2

Postoptimality Data

Objective	Unit Profit	Parameters
Transportation	$-c^t$ = \$400,000	$\tau = 1/2.9$ $\sigma = .386$
Utilities		$\tau = 1/2.9$ $\tau' = 5280$ $\sigma = .386$
Storm Sewers	$-c_1$ = \$100	
Sanitary Sewage	$-c_2$ = \$3.5	
Manholes	$-c_3$ = \$8/3	
Water	$-c_4$ = \$2.3	
Hydrants	$-c_5$ = \$1.2	
Valves	$-c_6$ = \$1.2	
Sewage Treatment Plant	$-P_1$ = \$1,083,000	$a_1 = 10$
Reservoir	$-P_2 = \dfrac{\$1,000,000}{4.6}$	$a_2 = 4.6$
Open Space	$-P_3$ = \$2,000	

Planned Development

One of the purposes of the model is to aid developers in their
efforts to prepare a land use plan that will ultimately be submitted
to the proper authorities for approval. It is important that the ramifications of any such plan be understood by those submitting the plan.
With the aid of Table 4.3 (a) and Table 4.5, which summarize the
solution to the primal problem (the figures reported have been rounded
off to the nearest integer, consequently the solution may not be
feasible in an LP sense), the land use plan generated for the proposed
development of an estimated 100,000 people will be considered, as
will the ramifications of this plan.

Table 4.3(a) contains the most profitable population size that
should be planned for. The dwelling mix, densities, and population
distribution within the planned development are no more or less than
explicit guidelines that are intended to serve as an aid to the developer
in his innovative efforts. The land use plan generated for the planned

TABLE 4.3

Optimal Distribution of Population in Planned Development

(a)

Variables Basic

Number of ---- Occupying Type X_{ij} Dwelling:	Type Dwelling				Slack* Associated with Basic Variables (type and number of people overplanned for)			
	X11	X13	X23	X33	X11	X13	X23	X33
Residents	19,471	42,660	15,220	15,220		7429	0	0
Manufacturing and Warehousing Employees	1,168	2,560	913	914		445		
Elementary School Students	3,245	7,110	2,537	2,537		1371		
Junior and Senior High School Students	2,488	5,451	1,945	1,945		1051		
Community College Students	378	830	296	296		0		
Marginal Profit								
Associated with ---- in Dollars per ---- Planned for:								
Type X_{ij} Resident	0		262	192				
Manufacturing and Warehousing Employees		0						
Elementary School Students		0						
Junior and Senior High School Students		0						
Community College Students		89,726						
Density (number families per acre)	7.3	4.8	19.4	54.3				

*People for whom schools, homes, and so forth are not built, i.e., less homes and the like than originally anticipated would be built.

(Continued)

TABLE 4.3 (Continued)
(b)

Variables Nonbasic

(0)	(1)	(2)
Type Dwelling	Number of (0) Built	Reduced Profit of (0) in Dollars per (0) Added
X12	0	89
X21	0	6,323
X22	0	2,905
X31	0	1,960
X32	0	1,230

development [Table 4.4, columns (3) and (4), and Table 4.5] gives
the optimal allocation of land over the various uses. On the surface
this land use plan, with its associated number of various elements to
be supplied, appears routine. But the allocation of land in a planned
development is dictated by the technical coefficients, which determine
the type of environment of the planned development. The technical
coefficients are a direct result of both the developer's conception of
(a) what the development should consist of, and (b) the relationship
among the various elements considered and the social and natural
characteristics of the region, which dictate existing or potential
relationships, as well as interrelationships. Therefore, the land
allocated over the various uses is the result of a multitude of factors—
the ultimate effect of which is to specify the type of environment for
the planned development.

Finally, with an understanding of the implications and interactions
characteristic to any particular land use plan, the plan may be modified
as given or may serve as a check for changes made by the parties
involved. Proposed changes in land use are easily conducted and
evaluated within the framework of the model. For instance, $\alpha(v)$ gives
the proportion of the total available land (A) that is used for a particular use, v. If, for a specified use, the land allocated to it, $\alpha(v)A$,
where v takes on a specific value), is judged to be too great, then this
particular land allocation can be controlled by specifying the maximum
proportion of land that is to be used, thereby constraining its upper
limit in the model.

Planned Development Economics. The financial consequences of
undertaking a planned development are not independent of the land use

TABLE 4.4

Optimal Land Use Plan for the Planned Development

(0) Index of Land Uses v=	(1) Land Uses	(2) Proportion of Total Available Land Used for Use v [α_v]	(3) Land Used for (1) in Acres [$\alpha_v A$]	(4) Number of (1) Built	(5) Marginal Profit Associated with (3) in Dollars per Total Acre [u_1^*]	(6) Land Development Values for Land Used for Use (1) Dollars per Acre Used for Use (1) [u_v^*]
	Dwellings:					
1	x11	.55213	741	5,409	$11,739	$ 21,261
	x13		2441	11,850		311,134
2	x23	.03773	217	302	11,739	869,563
3	x33	.01350	78	846	11,739	
4	Manufacturing and Warehousing	.06023	347	n.a.*	11,739	194,904
	Schools:					
5	Elementary	.04239	244	23	11,739	276,931
6	Junior and Senior High	.03539	204	7	11,739	331,707
7	Community College	.01735	100	1	11,739	676,605
	Commercial Establishments:					
8	Neighborhood Shopping Center	.05140	296	4	11,739	228,387
9	Town Shopping Center	.01205	69	1	11,739	974,199

(0)	(1)	(2)	(3)	(4)	(5)	(6)
Index of Land Uses v=	Land Uses	Proportion of Total Available Land Used for Use v $[\alpha_v]$	Land Used for (1) in Acres $[\alpha_v A]$	Number of (1) Built	Marginal Profit Associated with (3) in Dollars per Total Acre $[u_1]$	Land Development Values for Land Used for Use (1) Dollars per Acre Used for Use (1) $[u_v^*]$
	Public Services:					
10	Fire/Police/Office Buildings	.00313	18	12	$11,739	$ 3,750,511
11	Garages/Depots	.00312	18.5	4	11,739	3,657,040
	Health Services:					
12	Clinics	.00161	9.3	9	11,739	7,291,366
13	Hospitals	.00642	37	1	11,739	1,828,520
	Parks and Recreational Areas:					
14	Tot Lots	.00803	46	n.a.	11,739	1,461,905
15	Playgrounds	.02409	139	n.a.	11,739	487,302
16	Neighborhood Parks	.03212	185	n.a.	11,739	365,474
17	Playfields	.02409	139	n.a.	11,739	487,302
18	Community Parks	.05622	324	n.a.	11,739	208,806
	Cultural Facilities:					
19	Performing Arts Center	.00039	2.2	1	11,739	30,100,256
20	Libraries	.00111	6.4	5	11,739	10,575,765
21	Cemeteries:	.00418	24	n.a.	11,739	2,808,397
22	Churches/Houses of Worship	.01324	76	37	11,739	886,639

*Does not apply.

45

TABLE 4.5

Infrastructure Usage as Determined
from Optimal Land Use Plan*

	Transportation, Number of Lineal Miles for (0)	Utilities		Land Used for (3) (acres)
		Number of Lineal Feet for (1)	Number of (2) Supplied	
(0) Roads	769			
(1) Storm Sewer System		4,059,046		
Water System		4,059,046		
Sanitary Sewage System		4,059,046		
(2) Manholes			13,530	
Hydrants			8,118	
Valves			16,236	
(3) Sewage Treatment Plant				10
Reservoir				4.6
Open Space				3139.7

*Optimal land use plan referred to is Table 4.4.

plan or changes made to this plan. Rather, the financial implications
of any particular plan should be instrumental in guiding the developer
in making appropriate changes. Since this example involves an
"instant city," the question of the time value of money does not arise.

For the example being considered, the maximum profit and return
on total investment to the developer undertaking the planned development are, respectively, $144,591,311 and 11.1 percent. These
figures are obtained from the development and municipal account
summary (Table 4.6). It is of interest to note that, if the municipality
had not incurred the expense of either the roads or utilities, the

TABLE 4.6

Development and Municipal Account Summary
(a)
Development Account Summary

Net Profit from LP Solution		$ 236,082,848.00
Investments Considered in Obtaining Net Profit:		
Housing	$ 559,932,625.67	
Industry	183,975,486.27	
Commercial	211,558,063.74	
Other*	249,460,045.26	
Subtotal	$1,204,926,220.94	
Other Investments:		
Reservoir	$ 1,000,000.00	
Open Space	6,279,400.00	
Sewage Treatment Plant	10,830,000.00	
Subtotal	$ 18,109,400.00	
Cost of Financing (@ 6%)	$ 73,382,137.26	
Total Investment		$1,296,417,758.20
True Profit: (net profit—other expenses—financing cost)		144,591,311.00
Percentage Return on Total Investment	11.1%	

(b)
Municipal Account Summary

Investments:	
Roads	$307,503,448.28
Utilities	450,012,846.34
Total:	$757,516,294.62

*Refers to investments in schools, services, facilities, cemeteries, and churches.

developer would incur a substantial financial loss as a result of his undertaking. This point further substantiates the ample literature that refers to the plight of developers who would attempt to undertake such an endeavor with little or no external aid.

Noticeably missing from the optimal land use plan were several dwelling types that had been considered. Those dwelling types that are in solution [Tables 4.3(a) and 4.4] suggest the most favorable dwelling mix and density to employ. In contrast, those that are not in solution [Table 4.3(b)] reveal not only the least profitable dwelling types, but the degree to which each would decrease the profit if they were forced into solution. Also, since these dwelling types are considered unfavorable from the profit maximization point of view, then the corresponding average lot sizes associated with each dwelling type must be deemed unfavorable as well. This very fact represents an additional guide to the developer.

Another measure that provides the developer a means for judging the worth of his plan is what are commonly referred to as the marginal profits [Tables 4.3(a) and 4.4]. These values arise when the constraints in the model are satisfied as equalities, i.e., since the resources are completely utilized, the developer has not exhausted his need for this resource and is willing to pay some unit price for an additional unit. Alternatively, the marginal profit may be considered as the profit foregone for each unit of a scarce resource not made available. In order to understand the significance of these values—in particular, that associated with community college students—it is necessary to recall the interrelatedness of the problem, i.e., the failure to provide for one more community college students leads to fractional decreases in the number of other elements that would otherwise be supplied. The ultimate effect is that a profit of $89,726 is foregone for each such student not planned for.

From Table 4.4 it is apparent that the profit foregone is the same for each use (constraint) but it is not apparent that the value of $11,739 is the profit foregone for each total acre not developed, i.e., it is not the profit foregone for each acre not made available for use v; rather, it is independent of each of these uses. This point will be discussed further under planned development evaluators, as will land development values, a final measure of the economic worth of a land use plan.

Planned Community

It has been suggested that the objective of a planned community is some measure of social welfare. Clearly, if this is true, then this measure, or objective, must reflect the social cost incurred by developers of planned communities, as well as the benefits to be

derived by the residents of these communities. To see this it is
necessary to consider the dual of the primal problem (planned development). In the context of the dual problem, these marginal profits have
greater intuitive appeal if interpreted as the imputed price the
developer must pay for a unit of the scarce resource. The objective
of the dual problem is to minimize these imputed unit prices such
that the value of the resources to the developer is at least as great
as the unit profit derived from using them. If the imputed unit cost
is strictly greater than the unit profit, then the associated decision
variable will be nonbasic, i.e., no type $X_{i,j}$ dwellings will be built.
This explains why the dwelling types shown in Table 4.3(b) were not
in solution and a reduction in profit would result from forcing them
into solution.

This observation and the conclusion previously drawn was for
a planned development, where the objective was to maximize profits.
In a planned community undertaking, however, it may be desirable
to have one or more of the dwelling types shown in Table 4.3(b) in
solution. Assume that one or more of these dwelling types are forms
of middle-income housing. It has already been shown that the cost
of providing these dwellings will exceed any profit that will result
from their sale. In order to provide such dwellings it is customary
for developers to work under the auspices of federal programs, such
as sections 235 and 236 of the Housing and Urban Development Act
of 1970, depending on whether the dwellings are for rent or sale.
Provision of dwellings under these programs would result in lower
profits than could be obtained from sales to exclusively high-income
groups. But in a planned community the objective is to maximize
social welfare through the provision of welfare attributes, such as
middle-income housing. It follows that the developer incurs a social
cost for providing such dwellings, which is reflected in reduced
profits, while less-prosperous families derive the benefit of having
their own home or, at the very least, a form of shelter that they can
take pride in.

Planned Development Evaluators. From established duality relationships we know that the optimal values of the dual evaluators, u_1^* and
u_2^*, where u_1^* is the $(k'+q')x1$ vector (the dimensions on these vectors
are those derived in Appendix 4.1) and u_2^* is a scalar, provide an
allocation or imputation of the net profit ($236,082,848 in the example)
to the resources. Consequently, the net profit is completely exhausted,
and there exists a one-to-one correspondence between the resources
and the allocation of the net profit to these resources.

In order to appreciate the meaning of these dual evaluators, it
is necessary to perform a dimensional analysis on u_1^* and u_2^*. The
dimensions of all terms in the primal problem are known, i.e.,

α_v = the proportion of the total available land used for use v,

1 = the proportion of the total available land used,

c_v^T = dollars per proportion of the total available land used for use v,

A_{12} = total available land,

B_v = total land available for use v,

A_{22} = the proportion of the total available land used / the proportion of the total available land used for use v.

These dimensions refer only to the vectors and matrices dealing with land use. The first k' values in the vector u_1^* deal with the imputed value of population resources [as reported in Table 4.3(a)] and are not being considered here, for they pose no unique interpretation. The q' terms in the vector u_1^* (reported in Table 4.4) are being considered here, and any future statements will pertain to these only.

From the dimensions of the selected terms and the structure of the dual problem, the dimensions of u_1^* and u_2^* are, respectively, dollars per (total available acre)·(proportion of the total available land used for use v), i.e., $\$/\alpha_v$. (total available acre), and dollars per proportion of the total available land used. The value of u_2^* has not been tabularly reported, but from the solution output was found to have a value of $67,656,130.

Therefore, $u_2^* = \$67,656,130$ is the minimum cost the developer places on developing the total land that has been acquired. It also represents that portion of the net profit, derived from saleable properties, which has been allocated, in aggregate, to the total available and developed land. It is also possible to determine the cost or value placed on developing an acre of land for a specific use, v. First, it is necessary to consider u_1^*, which from the solution output is known to have a value of $\$11,739/\alpha_v$. (total acres available).

From the structure of the dual problem and the fact that each element of the vector c_v is zero, the inequality $u_1^* \geq (A_{12}^T) - 1\,A_{22}^T$ u_2^* holds. It is apparent that each element of u_1^* is the value placed on acquiring an acre of land without regard to a specific use. The usefulness of u_1^* in providing any insight into the problem is limited. But, it does offer the means by which values can be placed on the development of land for various uses.

These values, u_v^* (reported in Table 4.4), are herein referred to as land development values and are readily determined from u_1^*. It is important to note that u_2^* is an upper bound on the elements of the vector u_v^*.

u_v^* is obtained by expressing α_v in u_1^* [11,739 per α_v. (total available acres] in terms of the total land used for use v per total available land $\dfrac{\alpha_v A}{A}$ and then reducing u_1^* to the dimension dollars per acre used for use v.

Of the $236,082,848 net profit, all but $67,656,130 was imputed to the population resources. The per unit allocations are shown in Table 4.3(a) (marginal profits). The addition of any one of these resources is of benefit to the developer, insofar as they would increase his profit.

Among the various land uses only several lead to a direct profit to the developer. The land development values indexed by v = 1, 2, 3, 4, 8, and 9 (Table 4.4) are of particular concern, for they indicate which of the land uses contribute most to profit.

Land used for facilities, services, amenities, and the like also have values imputed to them. These values are most logically interpreted as the value residents place on having land devoted to these uses. In other words, the land development value represents that amount which residents, in aggregate, would have to pay for having land developed for the specified use. Their willingness and ability to pay would confirm that they do, in fact, place a value u_v^* on land developed for use v. This is precisely what is being done in Columbia, Maryland. Recreation and community facilities are being developed under the auspices of the Columbia Park and Recreation Association, with the objective of providing a better living environment. To finance this work a user fee is required, and an annual charge is levied at the rate of $.75 per $100 assessed valuation on all taxable real estate properties. Thus, Columbia represents a current example where residents have placed a value on land developed for special uses.

The sale prices of residential, commercial, and industrial properties were arrived at by assuming some mark-up over the cost incurred in developing these saleable properties. Also, no profit was derived from the development of land for special uses. The land development values, therefore, would represent those additional charges, in the form of user pay fees and annual charges, which would be required to meet the various operating expenses (debt service, maintenance, and so forth) customarily associated with such uses. Finally, these additional charges are customarily imposed to the extent that the special uses can be provided on a break-even basis.

PLANNED DEVELOPMENT AND PLANNED
COMMUNITY: A COMPARISON

It was originally proposed that a developer was to undertake a planned development. To ensure the ultimate success of his endeavor, certain political and marketing constraints were imposed on the development, i.e., the provision of services, facilities, amenities, and so forth.

From analyzing the dual evaluators, it was seen that these constraints are, in part, social constraints. It was seen from the dual that the special uses are provided on a break-even basis and, as such, represent both a benefit to the users and a social cost to the developer. Both of these satisfy the objective of a planned community, i.e., maximization of social welfare. The social constraints, originally imposed for reasons completely unrelated to improving social welfare, have the effect of decreasing the economic gain to the developer. This is easily seen if the land being used for some special use were instead used for saleable properties or not used at all.

A planned development and a planned community are ends of a spectrum. From the following illustration,

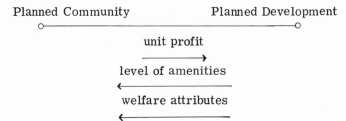

it is seen that the economic gain to the developer is decreased to the extent that social constraints are imposed on the planned development. A planned development in the strict sense would be one for which α_v, for all values other than v = 1, 2, 3, 4, 8, and 9, would equal zero (see page 44). Otherwise, the extent to which a planned community would be approached would depend on how the various elements of α_v were constrained.

Amenities (social constraints) are only one aspect of a planned community. A second would be the extent to which welfare attributes (e.g., middle-income dwellings) are provided. As was shown previously, the provision of such dwellings would be reflected in the objective function. Needless to say, land must be allocated for such dwellings. Thus, land allocated for welfare attributes may be considered a social constraint to the extent it is made available for such uses.

CONCLUSIONS

The purpose of this exposition has been twofold: (a) to establish the merit of linear programming as a methodology for aiding developers in their efforts to develop land use plans for planned developments, and (b) to establish the relationship between a planned development and a planned community. Examination and interpretation of the dual variables has been cursory and are considered in greater detail in Chapter 8.

Linear programming offers a potentially valuable tool for dealing with the complexities of large-scale developments. The use of linear programming not only serves as a guide to the developer but, more importantly, proposes a framework in which the complexities are recognized and the ability to deal with them constructively is improved.

An important implication of the analysis is that we need no longer be concerned with whether a new community is a planned development or a planned community. Rather, we know that a common methodology may be used to analyze the new community irrespective of its classification, provided we realize that the return expected by the development entity must be consistent with the nature of the new community (e.g., the location of the new community on the spectrum). That is, the implementation of social goals through physical innovations and the risk inherent therein must be reflected in the expected return, whether it be profit, rate of return, or some other economic measure.

APPENDIX 4.1

The "Instant City" Model*

The Model

The primal formulation of the model is
$$\text{maximize } C_1^T X + C_v^T \alpha_v$$
subject to $A_{11} X + A_{12} \alpha_v \leq B$

---

*The purpose of this appendix is to present the general description of the model. In addition, the specific constraints and objective function for the instant city new community are given.

$$A_{21} X + A_{22} \alpha_v = 1$$

$$X, \alpha_v \geq 0;$$

whereas the dual problem is

$$\text{minimize } B^T u_1 + u_2$$

$$\text{subject to } A_{11}^T u_1 + A_{21}^T u_2 \geq C_1$$

$$A_{12}^T u_1 + A_{22}^T u_2 \geq C_v$$

$$u_1 \geq 0 \text{ with}$$

$$u_2 \text{ free.}$$

In this formulation C_1^T is a lxnw vector of profit coefficients; X is a nwxl vector of decision variables (dwelling mixes); C_v^T is a lxq' vector of profit coefficients (zeros); α_v is a q'xl vector of decision variables (proportions); A_{11} is a (q'+k')xnw matrix of technical coefficients,

where $A_{11} = \begin{bmatrix} A_{11}^P \\ \hline A_{11}^L \end{bmatrix}$ and A_{11}^P is the k'xnw matrix of land absorption

coefficients; A_{21} is a lxnw vector of zeros; A_{12} is a (k'+q')xq' matrix

of technical coefficients, where $A_{12} = \begin{bmatrix} A_{12}^P \\ \hline A_{12}^L \end{bmatrix}$ and A_{12}^P is

a k'xq' matrix of zeros, whereas $A_{12}^L = - A$ times a q' x q' identity matrix; A_{22} is αlxq' unit vector; B is a (q'+k')xl vector of available resources, where B =

$\begin{bmatrix} B^P \\ \hline B_v^L \end{bmatrix}$, B^P is the k'xl vector of population resources, and B_v^L is a

q'xl vector of zeros; u_1 is a (k'+q')xl vector of the imputed values of the resources, where

$$u_1 = \begin{bmatrix} u_1^P \\ \hline u_1^{LD} \\ \hline u_1^{LR} \end{bmatrix}$$ and u_1^P is a k'x1 vector of the imputed values of popula-

tion resources to the developer, u_1^{LD} is a $(k+p-k')$x1 vector and u_1^{LR}
is a $[q'-(k+p-k')]$x1 vector, both of which give the imputed value per
total acre made available and are independent of the constraints;
however, $\frac{1}{\alpha_v}.u_1^{LD}$ gives the imputed values of land resources, used
for $(k+p-k')$ uses, to the developer and $\frac{1}{\alpha_v}.u_1^{LR}$ gives the imputed

values of land resources, used for $[q'-(k+p-k')]$ uses, to the residents;
and u_2 is the imputed value of the total land used per total land
available.

Constraints That Depend on the Planned
Population of the Development

(A.1) $\sum\limits_{j=1}^{w} O_{ij} X_{ij} \leq P_i^d$ $i = 1,2,...,n,$

where P_i^d is the population planned for i-type dwellings and O_{ij} the
number of people per i-type dwelling on lot size j.

(A.2) $P_t^Q Y \leq \delta_t (E-M),$ $t=n+1,...,\kappa,$

where P_t^Q is the number of people per unit employable in t-type industries; E is the forecasted new residents requiring employment;
M is the forecasted number of residents (E) that will be in the metropolitan area; and δ_t is the percentage of the labor force employable
in industry of type t.
    It is assumed without loss of generality that only light industry
will be supplied, since employment in heavy industry is to be found
among the M-employment opportunities in the metropolitan area.
Light industry will be supplemented with employment opportunities
in public services and commercial establishments.

(A.3) $r_\kappa^S Y \leq P_\kappa^S$ $\kappa = \kappa +1,...,\kappa',$

where r_κ^S is the number of κ-type students per unit; and P_κ^S is the student population planned for κ-type schools.

Constraints That Depend on the Land Usage

(A.4) $\qquad \sum_{j=1}^{W} a_{ij}^d X_{ij} \le \alpha_i A \qquad\qquad\qquad i=1,2,\ldots,n,$

where a_{ij}^d is the acreage used per i-type dwelling on lot size j.

(A.5) $\qquad P_t^Q a_t^m Y \le \alpha_t A \qquad\qquad\qquad\qquad t=n+1,\ldots,\kappa,$

where a_t^m is the acreage employed for t-type light industry per employed worker. The density $(a_t^m)^{-1}$ for the t-type industry, since it is light industry, is comparable to that found in industrial parks.

(A.6) $\qquad (n_\kappa^S)^{-1} r_\kappa^S)a_\kappa^S Y \le \alpha_\kappa A \qquad\qquad\qquad \kappa=\kappa+1,\ldots,\kappa',$

where n_κ^S is the number of students per κ-type school; and a_κ^S is the acreage used per κ-type school. Since it is common to combine junior and senior high school students into one structure, land will be absorbed for high schools.

(A.7) $\qquad L_c a_c^A P' Y \le \alpha_c A \qquad\qquad\qquad\qquad c=\kappa'+1,\ldots,p$

where a_c^A is the acreage used for c-type establishments per 1,000 people serviced; P' is the average family size per unit; and L_c is the percentage of the population that will be served by c-type establishments. Land used by a c-type establishment consists of the land for the establishment only, Y_c, and the land devoted to parking, which is given by the parking ratio, γ.

(A.8) $\qquad P' a_P^B Z_P^B Y \le \alpha_p A \qquad\qquad\qquad\qquad P=p+1,\ldots,p',$

where a_P^B is the acreage used per P-type service building; and Z_P^B is the number of P-type service buildings required per 1,000 population. It is herein assumed that public services are characterized by building types.

(A.9) $\quad a_H^L n_H^L P' Y \leq \alpha_H A,$ $\qquad\qquad H=p'+1,\ldots,h,$

where a_H^L is the acreage used per type H health facility; and n_H^L is the number of type H facilities required per 10,000 population.

(A.10) $\quad P' a_F^R Y \leq \alpha_F A,$ $\qquad\qquad F=h+1,\ldots,h',$

where a_F^R is the acreage used for a type F facility (public parks and recreational areas) per 1,000 population.

(A.11) $\quad P' a_\lambda^c n_\lambda^c Y \leq \alpha_\lambda A$ $\qquad\qquad \lambda=h'+1,\ldots,f,$

where a_λ^c is the acreage used per type λ cultural facility; and n_λ^c is the number of type λ facilities per 1,000 population.

(A.12) $\quad a_g' P' Y \leq \alpha_g A$ $\qquad\qquad g=f+1,\ldots,q,$

where a_g' is the acreage used for cemeteries per 1,000 population. Among the factors considered in determining the acreage of land required for cemetery use are the following: (a) the anticipated number of burials per year, and (b) the basis employed for calculating cemetery space, e.g., park lawn type.

(A.13) $\quad \phi a_m^H n_m^H P' Y \leq \alpha_m A,$ $\qquad\qquad m=q+1,\ldots,q',$

where a_m^H is the acreage used per church; n_m^H is the number of churches required per 1,500 people; and ϕ is the percentage of the population to be served by churches. Churches or houses of worship are treated in aggregate, i.e., no differentiation is made between religions, although such a treatment poses no difficulty.

(A.14)
$$\sum_{i=1}^{n} \alpha_i + \sum_{t=n+1}^{\kappa} \alpha_t + \sum_{\kappa=\kappa+1}^{\kappa'} \alpha_\kappa + \sum_{c=\kappa'+1}^{p} \alpha_c$$
$$+ \sum_{P=p+1}^{p'} \alpha_P + \sum_{H=p'+1}^{n} \alpha_H + \sum_{F=h+1}^{h'} \alpha_F + \sum_{\lambda=\kappa'+1}^{f} \alpha_\lambda$$
$$+ \sum_{g=f+1}^{q} \alpha_g + \sum_{m=q+1}^{q'} \alpha_m = 1.$$

$$(A.15) \qquad \frac{1}{\tau} \sum_{j=1}^{W} L_{ij}^{Td} X_{ij} \le \sigma \alpha_i A, \qquad\qquad i=1,2,\ldots,n,$$

where

$$L_{ij}^{Td} = \tau \sigma a_{ij}^{d},$$

and

τ = number lineal miles per acre,
σ = multiple of acreage for elements corresponding to that used for roads.

The Objective

$$Z' = \sum_{i=1}^{n} \sum_{j=1}^{W} P_{ij}^{d} u_{ij} X_{ij} + \kappa_o Y,$$

where

$$\kappa_o = \sum_{t=n+1}^{\kappa} c_t^{m} a_t^{m} P_t^{Q} + \sum_{\kappa=\kappa+1}^{\kappa'} c_\kappa^{s} r_\kappa^{s}$$

$$+ P' \sum_{c=k'+1}^{p} P_c^{A} + a_c^{A} + P' \sum_{P=p+1}^{p'} c_P^{B} a_P^{B} Z_P^{B}$$

$$+ P' \sum_{H=p'+1}^{h} c_H^{L} a_H^{L} n_H^{L} + P' \sum_{F=h+1}^{h'} c_F^{R} a_F^{R}$$

$$+ P' \sum_{\lambda=h'+1}^{f} c_\lambda^{c} a_\lambda^{c} n_\lambda^{c} + P' \sum_{g=f+1}^{q} c_g^{'} a_g^{'}$$

$$+ P' \sum_{m=q+1}^{q'} P_m^{H} n_m^{H},$$

and

P_{ij}^{d} = profit per i-type dwelling on lot size j,

c_t^{m} = profit per acre for t-type industries,

P_c^{A} = profit per acre for c-type establishments,

$-c_\kappa^S$ = profit per κ-type student,

$-c_P^B$ = profit per acre for P-type service buildings,

$-c_H^L$ = profit per acre for type H use,

$-c_F^R$ = profit per acre for type F use,

$-c_\lambda^c$ = profit per acre for type λ use,

$-c_g'$ = profit per acre of cemetery use,

$-P_m^H$ = profit per church.

In addition, the costs of the infrastructure must be considered. The investment associated with roads is given by

$$\tau \sigma C^t \bar{A},$$

where C^t = lxW row vector of cost per lineal mile =

$[c_1^t \, .. \, c_x^t \, .. \, c_W^t]$;

and

$$c^t = c_x^t \text{ for} \qquad\qquad\qquad x=1,2,...,W,$$

and

W = the number of various land uses excluding open space.

Also

$$
\bar{A} = \begin{bmatrix} Y & \begin{matrix} \sum\limits_{i=1}^{n} \sum\limits_{j=1}^{w} a_{ij}^{d} X_{ij} \\[2ex] \sum\limits_{t=n+1}^{K} P_{t}^{Q} a_{t}^{m} \\[3ex] \cdot \\ \cdot \\ \cdot \end{matrix} \\[4ex] \phi Y & \sum\limits_{m=q+1}^{q'} a_{m}^{H} n_{m}^{H} \\[3ex] & a_{1} \\[2ex] & a_{2} \end{bmatrix} = \text{Wxl vector of acreages used for all elements,}
$$

and

a_1 = acreage used for a sewage treatment plant,

a_2 = acreage used for a reservoir.

Similarly, the investment associated with utilities is given by

$$\tau \tau' \ ^{\sigma} C \ \bar{I} \ \bar{A},$$

where

C = lxw' row vector of cost per lineal foot

= $[c_1, c_2 \ldots, c_w']$,

w' = the number of utilities (see Table 4.2),

$\bar{I}$ = w' x W unit matrix,

$\bar{A}$ = W x 1 column vector previously defined.

The investment associated with a reservoir, sewage treatment plant, and open space are given, respectively, by (P_2 a_2), (P_1 a_1), and ($TA-(1+^{\sigma})$ $\underline{I}$ $\bar{A}$) P_3, where I is a lxW unit vector.

APPENDIX 4.2

Element Identification

Housing

i=1: single-family dwelling	j=1: 6,000 ft.^{2} lot =2: 7,500 ft.^{2} lot =3: 9,000 ft.^{2} lot
=2: two-story row house	j=1: 17,500 ft.^{2} lot =2: 24,500 ft.^{2} lot =3: 31,500 ft.^{2} lot
=3: five-story multifamily house	j=1: 2,000 ft.^{2} lot =2: 3,000 ft.^{2} lot =3: 4,000 ft.^{2} lot

Light Industry

t=4: manufacturing and warehousing

Schools

κ=5: elementary
=6: junior and senior high
=7: community college

Commercial

c=8: neighborhood shopping center
=9: town shopping center

Public Services

P=10: fire/police/office buildings
=11: garage/depot building

Health Services

H=12: clinic
=13: 400-bed hospital

Public Parks and Recreational Areas

    F=14: tot lot
    =15: playground
    =16: neighborhood park
    =17: playfield
    =18: community park

Cultural Facilities

    λ=19: performing arts center
    =20: library

Cemeteries

    g=21: cemetery

Houses of Worship

    m=22: church

APPENDIX 4.3

Basic Element Cost

Housing

		Cost per Unit	Mark-Up (percent)	Sale Price	(P^d_{ij}) Profit
i=1	j=1	$20,000	115	$23,000	$3,000
	=2	22,500	115	25,810	3,310
	=3	25,800	115	29,610	3,810
=2	j=1	15,000	115	17,220	2,220
	=2	17,300	115	19,900	2,600
	=3	19,240	115	22,180	2,940
=3	j=1	12,000	115	13,800	1,800
	=2	13,400	115	15,400	2,000
	=3	15,300	115	17,600	2,300

Unless stated otherwise, all costs include land acquisition, land development, and construction.

Industry

	(c_g)	(c_I)		(c_t^m)
	Cost per Gross Saleable Acre	Cost per Acre for Other Site Improvements	Mark-Up (percent)	Profit
t=4	$525,000	$5,000	170	$365,000

$$c_t^m = 170\% \ (c_g) - (c_g + c_I)$$

Schools

	Cost per Student	Profit $(-c_\kappa^S)$
κ=5	$2,034	$2,034
=6	3,334	3,334
=7	8,900	8,900

Commercial

	(c_g)	(c_I)		(P_c^A)
	Cost per Gross Leaseable Acre	Cost per Acre for Other Site Improvements	Mark-Up (percent)	Profit
c=8	$441,000	$140,000	200	$301,000
=9	463,000	105,000	225	472,000

$$P_c^A = (M\%)c_g - (c_g + c_I)$$

Public Services

	Cost per Acre	Profit $(-c_P^B)$
P=10	$104,000	$104,000
=11	6,500	6,500

Health Services

	Cost per Acre	Profit $(-c_H^L)$
H=12	$1,984,000	$1,984,000
=13	400,000	400,000

Public Parks and Recreational Areas*

	Cost per Acre	Profit $(-c_F^R)$
F=14	$10,000	$10,000
=15	10,000	10,000
=16	10,000	10,000
=17	10,000	10,000
=18	10,000	10,000

Cultural Facilities

	Cost per Acre	Profit $(-c_\lambda^c)$
λ=19	$1,750,000	$1,750,000
=20	4,020,000	4,020,000

Cemeteries**

	Cost per Acre	Profit $(-c_g')$
g=21	$4,000	$4,000

Churches or Houses of Worship

	Cost per Acre	Profit $(-P_m^H)$
m=22	$1,449,500	$1,449,500

---

*Cost includes land acquisition and development.

**Cost includes land acquisition and development.

Transportation*

	Cost per Lineal Foot	Profit $(-c^t)$
	$400,000	$400,000

Utilities**

	Cost per Lineal Foot	Profit
storm sewers	$100	$100 = -c_1$
sanitary sewage	3.5	$3.5 = -c_2$
manholes	8/3	$8/3 = -c_3$
water	2.3	$2.3 = -c_4$
hydrants	1.2	$1.2 = -c_5$
valves	1.2	$1.2 = -c_6$

Sewage Treatment Plant***

	Cost per Acre	Profit $(-P_1)$
	$1,038,000	$1,038,000

---

*It is assumed that all roads are 24-feet concrete paved, with a 60-foot right-of-way, the standard cost of which is as given.

**It has been estimated that for storm sewers, catchment basins, other elements, and an average pipe size of 48 inches, the cost would be as given. For sanitary sewage, using a 15-inch diameter pipe, the cost is estimated as given. It is estimated that manholes will be required every 300 feet, at a cost of $800. Excavation and piping for water is estimated at the cost given. Hydrants and valves are required every 500 and 250 feet, at respective costs of $600 and $300.

***It is estimated that ten acres will be required to build a sewage treatment plant, the cost of which is estimated to be $10.83 million.

Reservoir*

Cost per Acre	Profit $(-P_2)$
$1,000,000/4.6	$1,000,000/4.6

---

*It is estimated that for a depth of 10 feet, 4.6 acres will be required for a reservoir, the cost of which is estimated to be $1 million.

5

**THE LAND
DEVELOPMENT
PROCESS**

The purpose of this chapter is to summarize the land development process, focusing on the financial aspects. Works by R. B. Ricks [51], T. Dienstfrey [13], and O. J. Thorne [61] are primarily concerned with the financial aspects of this process. General Electric/Tempo, Real Estate Research Corporation and Decision Sciences Incorporated, has recently or is currently undertaking research on the question of financial analysis of new community development sponsored by the New Communities Office in HUD.

The material in this chapter is drawn from (a) literature previously cited; (b) The Community Builders Handbook [43]; (c) a programmed modification of a model constructed by General Electric [19] (a sample output is included in Appendix 5.1); (d) discussions with new community developers at Columbia, Maryland, and Coral Springs, Florida; officials in the New Communities program at HUD; and bankers, realtors, and developers; and (e) participation as the coresponsible party for the financial analyses of a prospective new community in the capital district region (Albany, Rensselaer, Saratoga, and Schenectady counties, New York), the Highlands project [58]— this participation included working with staff members for Real Estate Corporation and Richard P. Brown and Associates, firms with extensive knowledge of new communities.

This experience helped clarify the meaning of financial feasibility. Financing is a major problem confronting community developers, but is solely concerned with the types of financing, i.e., equity, long-term debt and the like, and with various tax ramifications. Feasibility of a project is a much broader concern and must include (a) market feasibility—the composition of the market must be projected and a determination made of what segment(s) the new community will attempt to capture, including the need for low- to moderate-income housing; (b) fiscal feasibility—the financial impact of the proposed development on the appropriate public bodies must be evaluated; also, those services provided by the development entity (or some community association) in addition to, or in lieu of, the municipality must be delineated and costs and revenues forecasted; and (c) financial feasibility—this is concerned with the costs and revenues to the development entity, which may include (1) landowners, (2) developer, (3) builder(s), and (4) financial institution(s).

Current analytical approaches usually consider just financial feasibility and, if concerned with the others, do not integrate the results, e.g., the interrelationships among market analysis, the development schedule, and the financial feasibility of the project. More specifically, those models fail because (a) they treat the results of the market analysis deterministically and usually assume it is feasible and (b) they are incapable of performing sensitivity analyses on any of the components of the land use plan, market analysis, and so forth.

The multi-period linear programming model developed in Chapter 6 addresses itself to this failure, which is characteristic of all financial models. Neither linear programming nor cash flow analysis used alone can deal adequately with the problem of financial planning, but if both techniques are used in concert, the integration of all three feasibility analyses is possible. This is the subject of Chapter 7.

Any feasibility analysis, if not abridged, has four components: (a) market forecasts and land use data, (b) revenues, (c) investments and costs, and (d) financial analysis, composed of profit and loss statements, cash flow analyses, and financial measures of performance. Figure 5.1 illustrates the interrelationships among the various components.

The discussion to follow describes the land development process, using Figure 5.1 and Appendix 5.1 as frames of reference.

MARKET ANALYSIS

The material for this section is drawn from references [58] and [43], and, as noted in the latter, the prospective developer should determine the market demand within a region before accumulating land. However, this position is not always possible; in many cases the developer has some land or options on a particular site prior to undertaking a detailed market study—as noted in Chapter 2.

After defining the region under study (a somewhat arbitrary but important delineation), the following factors must be considered:

FIGURE 5.1

Financial Analysis Flow Chart

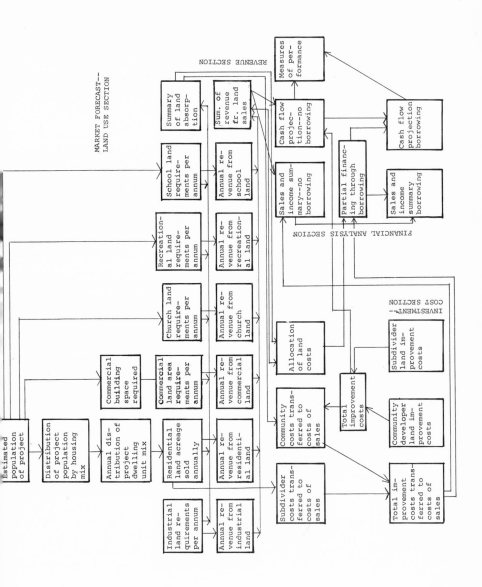

69

Population Growth

Population growth and its location within the region must be compared to national trends. This comparison will reveal the extent and importance of the growth. Population growth (or the lack of it) is a function of two major factors: (a) the rate of natural change in population, i.e., births and deaths, and (b) the rate of in- and out-migration, which is a minor component in national growth but a major factor in regional analysis. The trend difference in the first factor identifies the future population mix, i.e., in terms of age groups. This aids in determining the projected need for housing, employment, schools, services, and so forth.

Information on migration can provide insights into the relative attractiveness of the region. Trends in mobility by age groups specify the tenure by type of dwelling unit for the future housing market.

Family Formation

A key variable in determining the future housing market is the number and preference of individuals between the ages of fifteen and thirty-four, see [58], the years of family formation. Demographic analysis can give an estimate of the number in this age group, but a closer analysis is needed to identify preferences. The preferences of this group, those between the ages of thirty-five and sixty-four and those over sixty-five do change, whether measured as (a) staying within the family unit; (b) desiring to own or rent; (c) desired size of family; type dwelling desired; or (d) size lot preferred. These and similar preferences must be determined for the region and translated into future demand for housing by size, type, number, and tenure.

Housing Inventory

An analysis of the current housing in the region is an important guide in determining the types of dwellings that will be marketable in the future. This inventory must not only determine the number of dwellings in the region that are substandard and will require replacement, but must note local preferences, prejudices, and customs. If innovations are to be considered for the future, either in construction, design, or land use, then account must be made for merchandizing and management in order to inform the public of the advantages of the innovation. Among other inputs required for a complete market analysis are estimates of the present market value

of dwellings by type, the number of people currently residing in a
given type dwelling unit, and the size of dwelling units. This information, when combined with data on family formation, identifies
the size of dwelling units (number of bedrooms) that can be marketed.

Occupations

Identifying the future composition of the labor force serves
two purposes: (a) it provides information on the price range and
marketability of different types of dwelling units; and (b) it shows
the availability of labor by skills for prospective industry or government for a new community. Present and future employment
opportunities should be categorized as basic—those industries which
produce goods or services that are distributed outside the local
area—and secondary—those industries serving the basic industries
and local market. Although it is difficult to arrive at precise measures,
information on growth (or stagnation) of basic industries is key in
determining the future economic health of the region.

Market analyses for new communities also require a careful
assessment of the prospects of attracting new industry to the area.
Information on the labor market is as important a factor as site
availability, transportation, and so forth in the decision-making
processes involved in plant location.

Income Distribution

Once the projected population has been categorized into age
groups, occupational desires, family size, and prospective tenure,
it is necessary to estimate the income levels for the projected population. Current trends with respect to income levels for various
forms of employment are considered in this task. Once these income
levels are estimated, a comparison with the data obtained in the
housing inventory must be made to establish the number of families
that will be able to afford housing in various price ranges. Establishing these income levels is also necessary in determining the
potential spending pattern for goods and services.

A DEMAND SCHEDULE

Converting the projections into a housing demand schedule
requires estimating what fraction of the total regional growth could
realistically be captured (capture rate) for each year of the proposed

project. Factors such as past performance, access to employment opportunities, accessibility in terms of transportation networks, current construction in the county, and so forth are involved in estimating a capture rate. The estimation process usually consists of two stages. First a forecast of the amount of population growth by age and income for a segment of the region containing the site (i.e., a county) is made, then the percentage of this population that can be "captured" by the site is estimated. This approach assumes that the project will not affect the growth of the surrounding area. However, due to the size, innovative plan, or appeal of the proposed project to specific market segments (i.e., young unmarrieds), the project could increase the capture rate for the surrounding area.

Population projections are further refined to population projections per annum for housing mixes (type dwelling units) by size (number of bedrooms) and tenure (owners or renters). The anticipated number of dwelling units that would have to be constructed to meet the projected demand is estimated by employing assumptions on the number of persons per household, by size and tenure. These estimates are chosen after due consideration is given to the number of persons per household in existing housing in the area and the projected family formation patterns. As a result of the assumptions, estimates, and the like employed to arrive at the housing demand for the site, it is not unrealistic to consider alternative assumptions on capture rates. The project duration is a function of the capture rate, but it can also be effected by various marketing strategies.

HOUSING-RELATED ACTIVITIES

Large-scale projects, such as new communities, require that the planners consider the interrelationships between residential development and the wide range of services, activities, and needs of the residents. The demand schedule arrived at in the preceding section is not just a projection of housing demand, but includes the need for employment, schools, activities, and services, all of which are a function of the anticipated population. The timing of these various housing-related activities are dependent on (a) the type of activity, and (b) the population required to support or justify the activity.

Industry

Since new communities attempt to provide an environment that is ecologically sound, it is reasonable to assume most new communities focus on attracting light industry, such as research and development, and light manufacturing for basic employment. The particular industries to be considered are a function of the characteristics of the projected population, i.e., age, sex, income, education, and so forth and the existing employment opportunities in the area. The actual timing of industry and other activities will be discussed in the section on land requirements.

Commercial

Secondary employment opportunities are required in order to provide services for the anticipated population. The extent to which these services can be provided are dependent on the following: (a) the total number of people who define the trading area, (b) the mean and aggregate income of the populace in the trading area, (c) their disposable income after taxes, and (d) their spending potential on a per capita basis for various types of goods and services.

Educational

Basic determinants for projecting the need for educational facilities are the following: (a) the number of students per capita in the surrounding area—these can be obtained from the U.S. census; (b) the number of persons per household for each of the various types of dwelling units being considered by size and tenure; (c) the percentage of students in a household, who are, on the average, in various types of schools, e.g., elementary, junior, or senior; and (d) the maximum number of students enrolled in a particular type of school.

Service-Oriented Activities

Municipal services, such as fire protection, police protection, and health services such as clinics and hospitals, depend on the size and complexion of the population. These services are generally characterized by building types, e.g., hospitals, police stations, and so forth. The number of buildings required is estimated, using appropriate standards, e.g., one clinic per 10,000 people, which can then be reexpressed on a per capita basis.

Facility-Oriented Activities

The need and provision of recreational facilities, such as golf courses, playgrounds, and cultural facilities such as churches and libraries, are estimated in the same manner as the need and provision of service-oriented activities.

LAND REQUIREMENTS

In the previous discussion it was implied that a specific site was not chosen but, instead, an area (or areas) within the region. The amount of land required for development is dependent on (a) assumptions or standards employed with respect to the land required for each of the uses considered, and (b) the amount of land that is not saleable but required for major roads, open space, and the like. The question of timing may be dealt with in various ways. The need for schools, industry, services, and so forth requires a certain number of residents before it is necessary to provide them. Also, the need for services converted into land use can vary with different levels of population. For example, it may be found that a secondary school is needed after the population of the new community has reached 5,000, but the next secondary school may not be needed until the population reaches 15,000. In addition, the building space requirement may differ at different levels of population. If the building space requirement for different types of services are determined in this fashion, the lead time required to purchase land and perform the necessary construction is also determined.

Residential

In the section concerned with a demand schedule, a demand schedule was established, but the land requirements were not given in terms of amount and timing. Before land requirements can be determined, density (the number of dwelling units by type to be placed on a plot of land) must be specified. In this discussion density will be defined as gross density, e.g., the plot of land will contain streets, as well as dwelling units. Also, different densities can be specified for the same type of dwelling unit. Among the factors that will affect the density of various types of dwelling units are the following: (a) the costs associated with making a lot available for building, (b) zoning requirements, (c) preferences as to the lot sizes by prospective residents, and (d) the price range within which dwelling units will be saleable. Once densities have been specified, time required to prepare the land for sale must be in accordance with the projected market demand. For residential development a minimum of a one-year lag will generally exist between the purchase of land for building and the sale of the dwelling unit after construction.

Industry

Industrial land requirements are determined by employing average employee density standards—the number of employees per gross acre—for each type of industry. If the number of employees per annum is a function of the population per annum, the gross acreage required on a per annum basis is computable. This gross acreage represents the land that is sold and can be subdivided into its actual uses, such as the amount of industrial building space used that is given by the floor to area ratio (FAR). The area devoted to parking and circulation is given as a percentage of the gross acreage or as a function of the number of employees—a specified number of square feet per employee. The area devoted for landscaping is then the difference between the gross acreage and the land required for both industrial space and parking. If a population level is chosen for the project, the employee density factor is applied to this level to determine the gross acreage of industrial land required for building. If a population level is not employed, then a decision must be made as to when land is to be sold for industrial use, so that employment opportunities are programmed along with residential growth.

Commercial

To establish commercial building space requirements, an estimate is required of that share of the market which can be expected to be captured for each type of commercial establishment being considered. The goods or services that are provided by the commercial establishments require a certain level of expenditure per square foot of sales space to justify the provision of this space. Therefore, the spending potential per capita, an estimate of market share captured, and the expenditure required per square foot of sales space will determine the square feet per capita for each type of commercial space. If a population level were chosen for the project, this standard would then be used to determine the commercial space requirements. Otherwise, the standard would be used to determine the per annum requirements for commercial space. The developer then must decide when and how much land should be sold for commercial uses in order to meet the needs of the anticipated population. The actual amount of land sold includes land for parking and circulation. The former can be obtained as a ratio of commercial space, e.g., two-to-one, and the latter can be expressed as a percentage of the combined area required for commercial space and parking.

Education

The basic standards required to determine the number of educational institutions that are needed to serve the educational needs of the projected student population was presented. The land required by each of these institutions is approximated by using standards—acres per institution—that are common to each of the institutions being considered. As before, land requirements can be determined at specified or annual population levels—in this case student population. In either case educational facilities are programmed so that they are available in advance of need.

Service-Oriented Activities

The land required by these activities (building types) is estimated by employing accepted standards—acres per building type for each type being considered.

Facility-Oriented Activities

The land required for these activities is either calculated on an acreage per building type basis or on an acreage per capita basis, depending on the type activity being considered.

It is assumed that each of the land uses discussed constitute, in total, the saleable land. The total land required for development, however, would include, in addition to this land, land for open space, major roads, a sewage treatment plant if required, and so forth.

LAND SALE PROCEEDS

Establishing sale prices for land for various uses is a very difficult task. Among the complications that are involved are the following: (a) the sale price must consider the cost involved in preparing land for sale; however, the development costs are unknown, and the actual land costs may not be known; and (b) since the time span of the project involves several years or more, the developer will experience rising construction costs, inflationary increases in costs and prices, natural increases in income, and so forth, all of which will affect the sale price for land in any given year. Discussions with people involved in new community developments reveal that there are many ways of dealing with these complications. One way is to estimate the actual costs and revenues that would be experienced today and then (a) attempt to project future costs and revenue streams by extrapolating past trends in income level gains, construction costs increases, and so forth; (b) calculate the future value of today's costs and revenues for each year to project completion; (c) assume the effects of inflation negate any increases in revenues or costs and the gains in revenues are due to a general appreciation in land sale prices, stemming from an increased market demand (possibility caused by the environment of project); (d) assume land sale prices increase by some prechosen increment each year to the project horizon (Appendix 5.1), and (e) assume the costs and revenues identified today will be the same for the duration of the project. All these approaches still require a means of determining the present costs and sale prices for land in the region. The various costs components and the manner in which their costs are calculated will be discussed in the section on investments and costs.

Various procedures are used by land developers to determine land sale prices. The procedure to be discussed was developed and tested in the case study (Chapter 9), "The Highlands Project" [58]. Prices for land can be estimated by consulting realtors who are familiar with the latest land transactions in the region. With this information it is possible to estimate a sale price for land for various uses. These estimates, however, are likely to be conservative, for land purchased by a builder in the context of a new community differs significantly from that which is typically acquired. The parcels in the proposed development are sold with improvements, such as a main sewer line, major roadways, and so forth, while a builder usually acquires land that is unimproved and, often, without appropriate zoning. Traditionally, the builder must assume the costs and risks of land acquisition, seeking suitable zoning and capital investments in land improvements. Purchasing parcels in a new community affords the builder the opportunity for significant cost savings and greatly reduced risk. These savings are reflected in the increased land sale prices that accrue to the developer or development entity.

Land sale prices in the context of a new community must include: (a) land acquisition costs—based on actual transactions or on assumptions that reflect the value of agricultural land in the area; (b) site improvement costs—computed directly from the development plan and sketch plan (discussed in the section on investments and costs); and (c) estimated operating expenses—these expenses include the management costs of selling, legal fees, administrative expenses, real estate taxes, and so forth and are borne by the development entity (freeing the builder from another cost burden). Except for real estate taxes these costs are estimated from discussions with consultants experienced in new community development. The total land development cost is computed and allocated by type of use by acreage, resulting in an average cost per acre. This figure is further refined for the residential portion of the development into a cost per dwelling unit.

The value of residential land is computed, as shown in the land value flow chart (Figure 5.2) and may involve several iterations before an acceptable land value is determined. The process is as follows:

Land Value Flow Chart

Blocks 1-5

The determination of land value requires information on (a) demand for dwelling types by size and tenure as presented in the development schedule; (b) income distribution of the residents of the proposed development; (c) preliminary sketch plan for the development; and (d) a determination of the market value of dwelling units in the proposed development.

Blocks 6-10

These steps represent the calculation of the price of the dwelling unit. This price is based on construction costs and land development costs, which consist of (a) land acquisition, (b) site improvements, and (c) operating expenses and profit. These costs are derived from the sketch plan, except for operating expenses and profit, which must be estimated in the initial run and recomputed.

Blocks 11-12

The price computed must be compared to the market value determined by the income distribution of the prospective residents and with opinions of realtors, bankers, and consultants. If the price is higher than the market value, a reevaluation of land development costs must be made, and, if necessary, changes in the sketch plan must follow.

FIGURE 5.2

Land Value Flow Chart

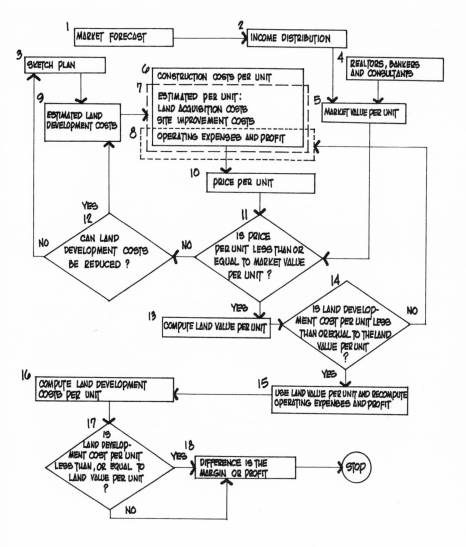

Blocks 13-18

    Land value is computed, based on the price of the dwelling;
real estate conditions in the area will stipulate what land values
average as a percentage of price. Land value then must be compared
to land development costs; if value is less than costs, operating
expenses (administration, legal, sales, and so forth) and profits must
be reevaluated. However, if land value is greater than development
costs, this value of the land is used in the calculation of the land
sales proceeds, and a recomputation of operating expenses is made.
Using this new value, the cycle is repeated, and if land value is again
greater than development costs, the difference is profit to the development entity. Note that this difference could be negative; the calculation
is complete.

    The estimated sale price per acre for land, other than residential,
is determined from consultations with consultants and realtors in
the area. Land sale proceeds are commonly assumed to be recognized on a 100 percent takedown cash basis at the time of the trans-
action. If desired, various assumptions can be invoked as to when
cash is received from the sale of land.

INVESTMENTS AND COSTS

    Four basic types of costs are incurred by the development
entity: (a) land acquisition, (b) investments in off-site improvements,
(c) investments in on-site improvements, and (d) operating expenses,
which are costs that are expended when land sales are made.

Land Investment

    Total investment for land acquisition may be determined in
several ways, depending on whether the development entity owns
or is purchasing the land. If the development entity owns the land
as a result of inheritances, gifts, or purchases conducted over a
period of many years, then the value used for land acquisition cost
is the current market value of the land. If land is being purchased
its actual cost is the proper investment figure. The total land required for development, if not already owned, can be determined
from a knowledge of the land required for the uses previously identified
and an estimate of nonsaleable land that will be required for open
space, major roads, and so forth.

    Although land may be purchased at various prices, it is common
to work with the average price paid per acre, once the total acreage

purchased and total costs are known or estimated from current land purchase transactions in the area.

On-Site and Off-Site Improvements

To determine the investments required for on-site improvements, it is necessary to prepare a sketch plan. Inputs required to prepare a sketch plan are the following: (a) total land required for development, and (b) development schedule, indicating the projected absorption of dwelling units by size, tenure, and number and the timing of housing-related activities, e.g., schools, commercial and industrial activities, and so forth. Using the development schedule and assumptions, or estimates, on densities and land absorptions per capita for various uses, a partial land use plan can be determined. From this plan appropriate lead times are considered for the various uses, such that improved land could be purchased and construction undertaken in order that dwelling units are available for sale and commercial establishments and so forth are available in accordance with the development schedule. This partial or incomplete land use plan contains the total amount of land that must be developed for each use in planning the project. These land use aggregates are called land allocations and equal the total amount of saleable land. For each land allocation planners decide the size of a development parcel and in what years these parcels are to be improved for subsequent sale as building lots. Although parcel sizes are a function of builder requirements and zoning developments, it is important to assure that improved parcels are available to meet the demand for improved land. Therefore, it is necessary to allow adequate time for the development of these parcels. Once the timing and sizes of parcels have been determined for the various land allocations, a land use plan is complete. The following bar chart illustrates the interrelationships between timing, land allocations, parcels, and so forth. The bar chart illustrates the requirement for lead times for various phases of the land development process. It should be noted that lead times are a function of the land use and will vary.

To arrive at a land use plan, it is necessary to determine the acreage required for the various uses and when it would be necessary to develop this land (required parcelization) in order to be available for sale in accordance with the development schedule. It is not necessary to consider the spatial location of these parcels on the site. If the demand schedule is to be met, it is necessary that on-site and off-site improvements be completed as programmed. Typically, off-site improvements include the following: (a) mass grading and clearing of all the land; (b) construction of major roads as required; (c) provision of main water lines, sewer lines, storm drainage lines, manholes,

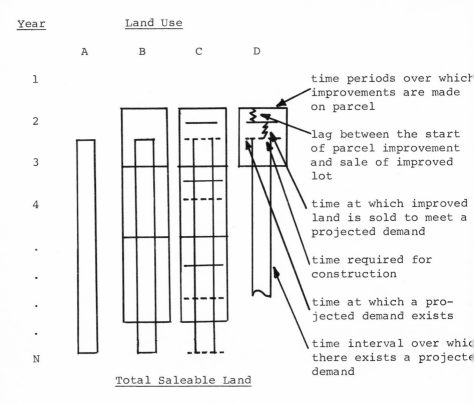

Year   Land Use

        A   B   C   D

1   time periods over which
                                         improvements are made
                                         on parcel
2
                                         lag between the start
                                         of parcel improvement
3   and sale of improved
                                         lot

4   time at which improved
                                         land is sold to meet a
                                         projected demand

.   time required for
                                         construction

.   time at which a pro-
                                         jected demand exists

.   time interval over which
N   there exists a projected
                                         demand
        Total Saleable Land

and utilities; and (d) complete land improvements for all uses other
than residential. The extent to which any particular improvement
will be required is dependent on the characteristics of the site, i.e.,
topology, geological factors, and so forth. The timing of off-site
improvements is dictated by both the temporal and spatial components of the sketch plan. The sketch plan translates the temporal
land use plan into a spatial-temporal plan for development. Once
parcels have been spatially located on the site, the timing of off-site
improvements must be programmed in order that the land is cleared,
major roads constructed, and so forth before on-site improvements
are started. The sketch plan permits estimation of both on-site and
off-site development costs.

On-Site Improvement Costs

For each residential parcel on-site improvements include all
improvements up to the boundaries of the various building lots.

Among the types of improvements that may be undertaken are the
following: (a) construction of streets; (b) provision of sidewalks,
curbing, lighting, water, gas, electricity, sewers, manholes, and
storm drainage; and (c) grading and clearing. In order to determine
the costs of improvements, it is necessary to estimate the extent to
which each of the improvements will be undertaken. The unit cost of
each of the improvements can be expressed in dollars per square
foot or dollars per lineal foot. Once the improvements to be undertaken are known and assumptions are made as to types of paving,
pipe sizes, thickness of paving, depth of cut for pipe laying, type pipe,
and so forth, the cost of improving the parcel can be determined. An
assumption usually employed is that, except for grading and clearing,
all other improvements follow the streets. The length of piping required for sewer or water laterals (i.e., piping running from the main
line to lot lines) is estimated by assuming that the length involved is
the same as, for example, the width of the street and sidewalk. To
determine the costs associated with street construction, it is necessary
to assume what the average width of streets will be. Many sources
are available for use in arriving at the unit costs to be employed in
the cost calculation. In the Highlands project publications from the
New York State Department of Transportation and the New York State
Office for Local Services, as well as the Marshall Valuation Service
[40], were most used.

Except for grading and clearing the costs of each of the other
types of improvements can be conveniently expressed in terms of
dollars per lineal foot of street for some average width. However,
in a preliminary analysis, such as that being discussed, the actual
length of streets in all the parcels is probably not known. Estimates
can be obtained by comparing these parcels with similar areas for
which the street lengths are known. From a knowledge of (a) the unit
cost of grading and clearing, (b) area to be graded and cleared, (c)
the unit cost of improvements per lineal foot of street, and (d) the
number of lineal feet of street per parcel, the on-site improvement
costs can be estimated for each parcel.

Off-Site Improvement Costs

Off-site improvements may be classified into three categories:
(a) mass grading and clearing of the site, (b) improvements related
to major road construction, and (c) improvements related to land uses
other than residential. Categories (a) and (b) are similar to the on-
site improvements, except parcels are not involved. The extent to
which improvements are required for uses other than residential
will depend on the use and the location of this use, e.g., if a shopping

center fronts a major roadway, then no additional street will be required. Improvements for these land uses will be discussed only to the extent that they differ from those previously presented.

Among the improvements typically incurred for industrial and commercial land uses are parking lot paving and lighting, the unit costs of which can be expressed in dollars per square foot. The unit costs, like all others, would include labor, materials, profit, overhead, and so forth. Provision of recreational facilities, such as a golf course, would require grading and clearing, complete sprinkler and drainage systems, planting of trees in open spaces, greens, tees, service roads, cart paths, and so forth, the cost of which can be expressed as dollars per hole. Lesser recreational facilities, such as playgrounds, baseball diamonds, and so forth, would probably require little more than grading and clearing.

Operating Expenses

As discussed previously, operating expenses are calculated as a percentage of land proceeds. The percentage used is based on discussions with consultants experienced in new community operations. It should also be noted that operating expenses are a function of land sale proceeds, and land sales prices are a function of all costs, including operating expenses. This is the major reason why the various comparisons shown in Figure 5.2 must be made.

Another cost component that must be included is that of real property taxes. Throughout the development period the developer will have land that remains to be improved and land that is improved, yet remains to be sold. In both cases this land is subject to taxation at its market value. The market value of unimproved land is taken as its current acquisition cost, whereas the market value of improved land is its current sales price. To determine the taxes that are paid annually, the combined county and town tax rates are applied to the assessed valuation of the land, i.e., the market value times the county equalization rate.

Housing Construction Costs

Although the new community developer is in the business of selling land, he must estimate the cost of housing that is planned for the site. From Figure 5.2 it was seen that the price for which the developer sells land depends on the market value of the dwelling to be built on it. The market value of the dwelling is the construction costs of the unit plus the per unit costs for land acquisition, site

improvements, and operating expenses. The construction costs should
include the following: (a) general building site preparation, including
excavation and leveling; (b) labor; (c) materials; (d) minimum landscaping; (e) architects and engineer's fees, (f) supervision, (g) administration overhead, and (h) permits and insurance. It should not
include land costs, nor any work beyond the lot line.

Costs Allocation

The allocation of costs to sales is required for a profit and
loss statement. It is discussed in this section, because it, like the
other costs and revenues, is an input into the financial analysis.
Some authors, see for example [13], dispense with considering cost
allocation in conducting financial analyses, for methods of cost
allocation are basically accounting issues, and, if the allocation of
costs are properly maneuvered, the true economic worth of the project
can be concealed for many years. G. M. Jones [34] proposed two
novel allocation schemes but felt that they could not be implemented.
One proposed costs should be allocated to sales based on some measure
of benefit for each site. In order to implement this approach, it
would be necessary to arrive at a measure of benefit. The second
scheme suggested was that cost be allocated on the basis of an expected
market value. However, there does not exist any theoretical justifi-
cation for such an allocation scheme.

Some method of cost allocation must be used if a profit and
loss statement is desired for financial analysis. The method chosen
is only constrained by accepted accounting principles. In Appendix
5.1 (a) the total investment in land was allocated in proportion to the
revenue derived from sales in each year, (b) the total investment
in off-site improvements was allocated in proportion to the total
acreage sold per annum from the total developed, and (c) the total
investment in on-site improvements was allocated in proportion to
the total residential acreage sold per annum from the total developed.

FINANCIAL ANALYSIS

Inputs into the financial analysis are the costs and revenues
resulting from development. The purpose of the analysis is to determine if the plan is financially feasible. If it is not it is necessary
to consider changes, e.g., decrease the development period, increase
densities, and so forth in order to arrive at a project that is financially
feasible. Although this approach is logical it may not be used. Alternatively, the financial analysis can become a mechanism for testing

those financial and accounting techniques that will yield a satisfactory rate of return for a given development plan. For example, legal tax shelter provisions that are in accordance with the Internal Revenue Service and state income tax codes can be assumed, with the effect that the payment of income taxes can be delayed for long periods.

The financial analysis presented in Appendix 5.1 to determine the financial feasibility of the project employs standard methods of cost allocation and is based on costs and revenues to be derived from development. In the case of financing assumptions are made as to the extent of financing required for land acquisition and improvements, with appropriate assumptions on interest rates. This type of analysis is important, for financing will be required, and the financial feasibility of the development plan must be evaluated in this light. More extensive analyses do not seem appropriate, for they do not recognize the importance of the development plan. The financial arrangements a developer will be able to secure will not depend solely on a development plan, but will consider the following: (a) his reputation, (b) his management skills and potential ability to carry out his project to a successful completion, (c) the existence or non-existence of federal support, and (d) the form of the development entity, generally characterized as being private, public, or a combination private-public entity.

The financial analysis is composed of three basic statements: (a) profit and loss statement, (b) cash flow statement, and (c) measures of performance. For land development projects they are related as follows: (a) the profit and loss statement is used to generate a schedule of taxable income, to which the appropriate federal and state income tax rates are applied to yield the required provision for taxes; (b) along with revenues, costs, and so forth, the annual provision for taxes is used in the cash flow statement to determine the per annum net cash flows to and from the project; and (c) the per annum net cash flow projection is the time series used to determine measures of performance, e.g., the discounted rate of return.

Profit and Loss Statement—No Financing

In the case of land development projects, the profit and loss statement is generated differently than that for income property developments. In the latter depreciation is deductible from net income to obtain taxable income and income tax, whereas in the former depreciation is replaced by book value—cost allocated to sales—in computing taxable income and income taxes.

Cash Flow Statement—No Financing

In this statement the actual per annum costs incurred for land acquisition, improvements, operating expenses, property and income taxes, and the change in working capital—if such a provision is made— are deducted from the per annum revenues from land sales in order to determine the net cash flows. Negative cash flows represent the net equity contributed to the project by the developer, whereas positive cash flows represent the yearly cash returns on that equity. Working capital represents those funds that are required to carry on the daily operations, i.e., finance sales, pay salaries, and so forth. Working capital needs may either be financed from equity contributions by the developer or through retention of a specified percentage of gross sales. The change in working capital in period t, if negative, denotes the decrease from year t-1 in liquid assets required to support working capital needs. If the change is positive in year t, then this would indicate the additional liquid assets over that required in period t-1 that would be needed to support working capital needs.

Profit and Loss Statement—Financing

This statement is exactly the same as for no financing, except for interest payments on land acquisition and construction loans, which are deductible from net income in determining taxable income and income taxes.

Land Acquisition Financing

Land acquisition loans are expressed as the amounts borrowed, i.e., a percentage of the land acquisition costs, and interest is paid on the average outstanding balance each year. These loans represent a line of credit, which is repaid as land sales are made, e.g., principal payments are made as a percentage of the land costs absorbed in sales each year.

Improvement Cost Financing

Construction loans are borrowings for off-site and on-site improvements, for which interest is paid on the average outstanding loan balance each year. The need for financing is a function of the annual unabsorbed land improvement costs. The extent to which construction loan financing can be undertaken is measured as a

percentage of the unabsorbed costs. Repayment of these loans are
subject to the same limit. The need for borrowing or the ability to
repay in any period t is given as the difference between the unabsorbed
improvement costs in periods t and t-1. A negative difference indicate
a need for borrowing and a positive difference the ability to repay
borrowings. The magnitude of each is given as the product of this
difference times the percentage of the unabsorbed land improvements
costs against which funds may be borrowed or repayed.

Cash Flow Statement—Financing

This statement is identical to that with no financing, except for
interest, which represents a cash outflow, and borrowings and repayments, which represent cash inflows and outflows, respectively.

Measures of Performance

Three measures are indicated in Appendix 5.1; however, a
program was written to compute the discounted rate of return only.
This was done because the primary measure of concern to both HUD
and the New York State Urban Development Corporation is that shown.
Mathematics are not required to determine the payback period; it
can be obtained by observation from the cumulative cash flow column,
where the payback period is the year in which the annual net cash
benefits equal the initial investment, i.e., cumulative cash flow equals
zero. The average rate of return on investment (accounting rate of
return) is commonly used in business and is the percentage of the
average annual net income after taxes to the average investment over
the life of the project. Both are easier to use than the internal rate
of return, but are not used for evaluating new community projects.
The payback period does not consider the time value of money, and
it does not consider the stream of income beyond the payback period.
The average rate of return overcomes the latter objection, but treats
present and future dollars as present dollars. The internal rate of
return is used because it considers the time value of money and is
that rate which equates the return of the accumulated after-tax (and/
or financing) dollars to zero and is a measure of return from the
project on the total cumulative investment in today's dollars. It
should be noted that the internal rate of return is not universally
used for both practical and theoretical reasons. For a discussion
of these, see A. M. Alfred and J. B. Evans [3].

APPENDIX 5.1

Sample Output from Financial Analysis Model*

		ESTIMATED POPULATION OF PROJECT PROPERTY							
	NUMBER D.U. AUTH IN REGION	PERSONS PER D.U.	REG. POP. INCREASE	REGIONAL POPULATION	PCT. PLAN AREA OF REG POP	PLAN AREA POPULATION	PROJ SHARE OF PLAN AREA INC	ANNUAL INC PROJECT POP	CUMULATIVE PROJ POP
1960	817	3.00	2328	148800	0.288	42854	0.00	0	0
1961	1411	3.00	4021	151128	0.286	43222	0.00	0	0
1962	2525	3.00	7196	155149	0.284	44062	0.00	0	0
1963	3008	3.00	9142	162345	0.282	45781	0.00	0	0
1964	1305	3.00	8672	171487	0.281	48187	0.00	0	0
1965	1305	3.00	3719	180159	0.280	50444	0.00	0	0
1966	1789	3.00	3719	183878	0.279	51301	0.00	0	0
1967	1789	3.00	5098	187597	0.277	51964	0.00	0	0
1968	1789	3.00	5098	192695	0.274	52798	0.00	0	0
1969	1789	3.00	5098	197793	0.271	53601	0.00	0	0
1970	1979	3.00	5640	202893	0.268	54374	0.00	0	0
1971	1979	3.00	5640	208531	0.267	55677	0.00	0	0
1972	1979	3.00	5640	214171	0.266	56969	0.39	503	503
1973	1979	3.00	5640	219811	0.265	58249	0.39	499	1002
1974	3898	3.00	11109	225451	0.264	59519	0.39	495	1497
1975	3545	3.00	10103	236560	0.277	65527	0.79	4746	6243
1976	3541	3.00	10091	246663	0.286	70545	0.70	3512	9755
1977	3899	3.00	11112	257754	0.294	75485	0.68	3359	13114
1978	3425	3.00	9761	267866	0.304	81431	0.48	2854	15968
1979	3305	3.00	9419	277627	0.310	86064	0.56	2594	18562
1980	3286	3.00	9365	287046	0.316	90706	0.49	2274	20836
1981	3601	3.00	10262	296411	0.319	94555	0.53	2039	22875
1982	3294	3.00	9387	306673	0.326	99975	0.53	2872	25747
1983	4274	3.00	12180	316060	0.329	103983	0.77	3086	28833
1984	4909	3.00	13990	328240	0.337	106616	0.76	5041	33874
1985	5253	3.00	14971	342230	0.347	118753	0.73	5940	39814
1986	5116	3.00	14577	357201	0.357	127520	0.65	5698	45512
1987	4980	3.00	14192	371778	0.366	136070	0.67	5728	51240
1988	4941	3.00	14081	385970	0.375	144738	0.71	6154	57394
1989	3925	3.00	11186	400051	0.381	152419	0.75	5760	63154
1990	4023	3.00	11465	411237	0.385	158326	0.00	0	63154
1991	3629	3.00	10342	422702	0.387	163585	0.00	0	63154
1992	3642	3.00	10379	433044	0.388	168021	0.00	0	63154
1993	3588	3.00	10197	443423	0.388	172048	0.00	0	63154
1994	3589	3.00	10228	453620	0.389	176458	0.00	0	63154
1995	3825	3.00	10901	463848	0.389	180436	0.00	0	63154
1996	3821	3.00	10889	474749	0.390	185152	0.00	0	63154
1997	3558	3.00	10140	485638	0.390	189398	0.00	0	63154
1998	3608	3.00	10282	495778	0.390	193353	0.00	0	63154
1999	3088	3.00	8800	506060	0.390	197363	0.00	0	63154
2000	0	3.00	0	514860	0.388	197765	0.00	0	63154
2001	0	3.00	0	514860	0.000	0	0.00	0	63154
2002	0	3.00	0	514860	0.000	0	0.00	0	63154
2003	0	3.00	0	514860	0.000	0	0.00	0	63154
2004	0	3.00	0	514860	0.000	0	0.00	0	63154
2005	0	3.00	0	514860	0.000	0	0.00	0	63154
2006	0	3.00	0	514860	0.000	0	0.00	0	63154
2007	0	3.00	0	514860	0.000	0	0.00	0	63154
2008	0	3.00	0	514860	0.000	0	0.00	0	63154
2009	0	3.00	0	514860	0.000	0	0.00	0	63154
TOTAL	128449		366060					63154	63154

*This output was generated from a programmed modification of a financial analysis model developed by the General Electric Company.

APPENDIX 5.1, continued

ANNUAL DISTRIBUTION OF PROJECT POPULATION HOUSING MIX

	PCT. POP. S.F. UNITS	PCT. POP. T.H. UNITS	PCT. POP LO-RISE	PCT. POP. OTHER	POPULATION S.F. UNITS	POPULATION T.H. UNITS	POPULATION LO-RISE	POPULATION OTHER	TOTAL POP. INCREASE
1970	0.00	0.00	0.00	0.00	0	0	0	0	0
1971	1.00	0.00	0.00	0.00	0	0	0	0	0
1972	1.00	0.00	0.00	0.00	503	0	0	0	503
1973	0.90	0.10	0.00	0.00	449	49	0	0	499
1974	0.90	0.10	0.00	0.00	445	49	0	0	495
1975	0.21	0.31	0.48	0.00	996	1471	2278	0	4745
1976	0.27	0.34	0.39	0.00	948	1194	1369	0	3512
1977	0.28	0.38	0.34	0.00	940	1276	1142	0	3359
1978	0.28	0.40	0.32	0.00	799	1141	913	0	2854
1979	0.29	0.39	0.32	0.00	752	1011	830	0	2594
1980	0.37	0.33	0.30	0.00	841	750	682	0	2274
1981	0.40	0.29	0.31	0.00	815	591	632	0	2039
1982	0.34	0.34	0.32	0.00	976	976	919	0	2872
1983	0.30	0.34	0.36	0.00	925	1049	1110	0	3086
1984	0.22	0.40	0.38	0.00	1109	2016	1915	0	5041
1985	0.24	0.42	0.34	0.00	1425	2494	2019	0	5940
1986	0.24	0.38	0.38	0.00	1367	2165	2165	0	5698
1987	0.22	0.33	0.45	0.00	1260	1890	2577	0	5728
1988	0.21	0.31	0.48	0.00	1292	1907	2953	0	6154
1989	0.19	0.31	0.50	0.00	1094	1785	2880	0	5760
TOTAL					16936	21814	24384	0	63154

ANNUAL DISTRIBUTION OF PROJECT DWELLING UNIT MIX

	PEOPLE/D.U. SINGLE FAM	PEOPLE/D.U. TOWN HOUSE	PEOPLE/D.U. LO-RISE APT	PEOPLE/D.U. OTHER	NO. UNITS SINGLE FAM	NO. UNITS TOWN HOUSE	NO. UNITS LO-RISE	NO. UNITS OTHER	TOTAL
1970	3.50	2.60	3.00	0.00	0	0	0	0	0
1971	3.50	2.60	3.00	0.00	0	0	0	0	0
1972	3.50	2.60	3.00	0.00	143	0	0	0	143
1973	3.50	2.60	3.00	0.00	128	18	0	0	145
1974	3.50	2.60	3.00	0.00	127	18	0	0	145
1975	3.50	2.60	3.00	0.00	284	565	759	0	1608
1976	3.50	2.60	3.00	0.00	270	459	456	0	1185
1977	3.50	2.60	3.00	0.00	268	490	380	0	1138
1978	3.50	2.60	3.00	0.00	228	438	304	0	970
1979	3.50	2.60	3.00	0.00	214	388	276	0	878
1980	3.50	2.60	3.00	0.00	240	288	227	0	755
1981	3.50	2.60	3.00	0.00	232	227	210	0	669
1982	3.50	2.60	3.00	0.00	278	375	306	0	959
1983	3.50	2.60	3.00	0.00	264	403	370	0	1037
1984	3.50	2.60	3.00	0.00	316	775	638	0	1729
1985	3.50	2.60	3.00	0.00	407	959	673	0	2039
1986	3.50	2.60	3.00	0.00	390	832	721	0	1943
1987	3.50	2.60	3.00	0.00	360	726	859	0	1945
1988	3.50	2.60	3.00	0.00	369	733	984	0	2086
1989	3.50	2.60	3.00	0.00	312	686	960	0	1958
TOTAL					4830	8380	8123	0	21333

(continued)

APPENDIX 5.1, continued

RESIDENTIAL LAND ACREAGE SOLD ANNUALLY

	SINGLE FAM UNITS/ACRE	SINGLE FAM ACREAGE	TOWN HOUSE UNITS/ACRE	TOWN HOUSE ACREAGE	LO-RISE UNITS/ACRE	LO-RISE ACREAGE	OTHER UNITS/ACRE	OTHER ACREAGE	TOTAL ACREAGE
1970	3.00	0	8.00	0	19.00	0	0.00	0	0
1971	3.00	47	8.00	0	19.00	0	0.00	0	47
1972	3.00	42	8.00	2	19.00	0	0.00	0	44
1973	3.00	42	8.00	2	19.00	0	0.00	0	44
1974	3.00	94	8.00	70	19.00	39	0.00	0	203
1975	3.00	90	8.00	57	19.00	24	0.00	0	171
1976	3.00	89	8.00	61	19.00	20	0.00	0	170
1977	3.00	76	8.00	54	19.00	16	0.00	0	146
1978	3.00	71	8.00	48	19.00	14	0.00	0	133
1979	3.00	80	8.00	36	19.00	11	0.00	0	127
1980	3.00	77	8.00	28	19.00	11	0.00	0	116
1981	3.00	92	8.00	46	19.00	16	0.00	0	154
1982	3.00	88	8.00	50	19.00	19	0.00	0	157
1983	3.00	105	8.00	96	19.00	33	0.00	0	234
1984	3.00	135	8.00	119	19.00	35	0.00	0	289
1985	3.00	130	8.00	104	19.00	37	0.00	0	271
1986	3.00	120	8.00	90	19.00	45	0.00	0	255
1987	3.00	123	8.00	91	19.00	51	0.00	0	265
1988	3.00	104	8.00	85	19.00	50	0.00	0	239
1989	3.00	0	8.00	3	19.00	0	0.00	0	0
TOTAL		1605		1039		421		0	3065

ANNUAL REVENUE FROM SALE OF RESIDENTIAL LAND

	SINGLE FAM $/ACRE	SINGLE FAM REVENUE	TOWN HOUSE $/ACRE	TOWN HOUSE REVENUE	LO-RISE $/ACRE	LO-RISE REVENUE	OTHER $/ACRE	OTHER REVENUE	TOTAL REVENUE
1970	$ 0	$ 0	$ 0	$ 0	$ 0	$ 0	$ 0	$ 0	
1971	$ 21500	$ 1010500	$ 27500	$ 0	$ 50000	$ 0	$ 0	$ 0	$ 1010500
1972	$ 22000	$ 924000	$ 29000	$ 58000	$ 50000	$ 0	$ 0	$ 0	$ 982000
1973	$ 22500	$ 945000	$ 30500	$ 61000	$ 50000	$ 0	$ 0	$ 0	$ 1006000
1974	$ 23000	$ 2162000	$ 32000	$ 2240000	$ 50000	$ 1950000	$ 0	$ 0	$ 6352000
1975	$ 23500	$ 2115000	$ 35000	$ 1909500	$ 50000	$ 1200000	$ 0	$ 0	$ 5224500
1976	$ 24000	$ 2136000	$ 35500	$ 2135000	$ 50000	$ 1000000	$ 0	$ 0	$ 5271000
1977	$ 24500	$ 1862000	$ 36500	$ 1971000	$ 51250	$ 800000	$ 0	$ 0	$ 4633000
1978	$ 25000	$ 1775000	$ 38000	$ 1824000	$ 53000	$ 717500	$ 0	$ 0	$ 4316500
1979	$ 25500	$ 2040000	$ 39500	$ 1422000	$ 54750	$ 583000	$ 0	$ 0	$ 4045000
1980	$ 26000	$ 2002000	$ 41000	$ 1148000	$ 56500	$ 602250	$ 0	$ 0	$ 3752250
1981	$ 26500	$ 2438000	$ 42500	$ 1955000	$ 58250	$ 904000	$ 0	$ 0	$ 5297000
1982	$ 27000	$ 2376000	$ 44000	$ 2200000	$ 60000	$ 1106750	$ 0	$ 0	$ 5682750
1983	$ 27500	$ 2875000	$ 45500	$ 4368000	$ 61750	$ 1980000	$ 0	$ 0	$ 9235250
1984	$ 28000	$ 3780000	$ 47000	$ 5593000	$ 63500	$ 2161250	$ 0	$ 0	$ 11534250
1985	$ 28500	$ 3705000	$ 48500	$ 5044000	$ 65250	$ 2349500	$ 0	$ 0	$ 11098500
1986	$ 29000	$ 3480000	$ 50000	$ 4500000	$ 67000	$ 2936250	$ 0	$ 0	$ 10916250
1987	$ 29500	$ 3628500	$ 51500	$ 4686500	$ 68750	$ 3417000	$ 0	$ 0	$ 11732000
1988	$ 30000	$ 3120000	$ 53000	$ 4505000	$ 70500	$ 3437500	$ 0	$ 0	$ 11062500
1989	$ 30500	$ 0	$ 54500	$ 0			$ 0	$ 0	
TOTAL		$42386464		$45619968		$25144976		$ 0	$113151408

(continued)

APPENDIX 5.1, continued

COMMERCIAL BUILDING SPACE REQUIREMENTS IN SQUARE FEET

	N.H. SHOP CTR. SPACE	COMM. SHOP CTR. SPACE	REGL SHOP CTR. SPACE	OFFICE SPACE-FT	MUN. BLDG SPACE-FT	HOTL/MOTL BLDG SPACE	COMM. REC. SPACE-FT	MISC BLDG BLDG SPACE	TOTAL SQ
1960	0	0	0	0	0	0	0	0	0
1961	0	0	0	0	0	0	0	0	0
1962	0	0	0	0	0	0	0	0	0
1963	0	0	0	0	0	0	0	0	0
1964	0	0	0	0	0	0	0	0	0
1965	0	0	0	0	0	0	0	0	0
1966	0	0	0	0	0	0	0	0	0
1967	0	0	0	0	0	0	0	0	0
1968	0	0	0	0	0	0	0	0	0
1969	0	0	0	0	0	0	0	0	0
1970	0	0	0	0	0	0	0	0	0
1971	0	0	0	0	0	0	0	0	0
1972	0	0	0	6500	0	0	0	0	5500
1973	0	0	0	0	0	0	0	0	0
1974	0	0	0	0	0	0	0	0	62000
1975	30000	0	0	0	10000	0	10000	12000	0
1976	0	0	0	0	0	0	0	0	112500
1977	30000	0	0	58500	20000	0	20000	24000	115000
1978	0	0	0	0	0	0	0	0	30000
1979	30000	10000	0	58500	20000	75000	0	24000	182500
1980	0	0	0	0	0	0	0	0	0
1981	0	0	0	0	0	0	0	0	40000
1982	50000	0	0	58500	20000	0	20000	24000	132500
1983	0	0	0	0	0	0	0	0	75000
1984	50000	0	0	58500	20000	75000	0	0	172500
1985	0	0	0	0	0	0	20000	24000	64000
1986	50000	15000	0	58500	20000	0	20000	24000	258500
1987	0	0	0	58500	0	0	0	0	122500
1988	50000	0	300000	58500	20000	75000	20000	24000	449000
1989	0	0	0	0	0	0	0	0	0
1990	0	0	0	0	0	0	0	0	0
1991	0	0	0	0	0	0	0	0	0
1992	0	0	0	0	0	0	0	0	0
1993	0	0	0	0	0	0	0	0	0
1994	0	0	0	0	0	0	0	0	0
1995	0	0	0	0	0	0	0	0	0
1996	0	0	0	0	0	0	0	0	0
1997	0	0	0	0	0	0	0	0	0
1998	0	0	0	0	0	0	0	0	0
1999	0	0	0	0	0	0	0	0	0
2000	0	0	0	0	0	0	0	0	0
2001	0	0	0	0	0	0	0	0	0
2002	0	0	0	0	0	0	0	0	0
2003	0	0	0	0	0	0	0	0	0
2004	0	0	0	0	0	0	0	0	0
2005	0	0	0	0	0	0	0	0	0
2006	0	0	0	0	0	0	0	0	0
2007	0	0	0	0	0	0	0	0	0
2008	0	0	0	0	0	0	0	0	0
2009	0	0	0	0	0	0	0	0	0
TOTAL									

Year	REGL S.C. LAND AREA	OFFICE LAND AREA	HOTL/MCTL LAND AREA	MISC. LAND AREA	PARKING LAND AREA	TOTAL AREA SQUARE FT	TOTAL ACREAGE	COMM LAND $/FT	COMM LAND REVENUE
1960	0	0	0	0	0	0	0	$0.00	$0
1961	0	0	0	0	0	0	0	$0.00	$0
1962	0	0	0	0	0	0	0	$0.00	$0
1963	0	0	0	0	0	0	0	$0.00	$0
1964	0	0	0	0	0	0	0	$0.00	$0
1965	0	0	0	0	0	0	0	$0.00	$0
1966	0	0	0	0	0	0	0	$0.00	$0
1967	0	0	0	0	0	0	0	$0.00	$0
1968	0	0	0	0	0	0	0	$0.00	$0
1969	0	0	0	0	0	0	0	$0.00	$0
1970	0	0	0	0	0	0	0	$0.00	$0
1971	0	0	0	0	0	0	0	$0.00	$0
1972	0	6500	0	1625	10400	18525	0	$0.70	$14820
1973	0	0	0	0	0	0	0	$0.80	$0
1974	0	0	0	15500	99200	114700	2	$0.90	$114730
1975	0	0	0	0	0	0	0	$1.00	$0
1976	0	58500	0	28125	180000	266625	6	$1.10	$319949
1977	0	0	37500	28750	184000	250250	5	$1.20	$325324
1978	0	0	0	7500	48000	55500	1	$1.30	$77699
1979	0	29250	0	45625	292000	366875	8	$1.40	$550311
1980	0	0	0	0	0	0	0	$1.50	$0
1981	0	0	0	10000	64000	74000	1	$1.60	$125799
1982	0	29250	0	33125	212000	274375	6	$1.70	$493873
1983	0	0	37500	18750	120000	176250	4	$1.80	$334874
1984	0	9750	0	43125	276000	328875	7	$1.90	$657748
1985	0	0	0	16000	102400	118400	2	$2.00	$248639
1986	0	9750	0	64625	413600	487975	11	$2.10	$1073541
1987	0	9750	0	30625	196000	236375	5	$2.20	$543650
1988	100000	0	37500	112250	718400	968150	22	$2.30	$2323552
1989	0	0	0	0	0	0	0	$2.40	$0
1990	0	0	0	0	0	0	0	$2.50	$0
1991	0	0	0	0	0	0	0	$2.60	$0
1992	0	0	0	0	0	0	0	$2.70	$0
1993	0	0	0	0	0	0	0	$2.80	$0
1994	0	0	0	0	0	0	0	$2.90	$0
1995	0	0	0	0	0	0	0	$3.00	$0
1996	0	0	0	0	0	0	0	$3.10	$0
1997	0	0	0	0	0	0	0	$3.20	$0
1998	0	0	0	0	0	0	0	$3.30	$0
1999	0	0	0	0	0	0	0	$3.40	$0
2000	0	0	0	0	0	0	0	$3.50	$0
2001	0	0	0	0	0	0	0	$3.60	$0
2002	0	0	0	0	0	0	0	$3.70	$0
2003	0	0	0	0	0	0	0	$3.80	$0
2004	0	0	0	0	0	0	0	$3.90	$0
2005	0	0	0	0	0	0	0	$4.00	$0
2006	0	0	0	0	0	0	0	$4.10	$0
2007	0	0	0	0	0	0	0	$4.20	$0
2008	0	0	0	0	0	0	0	$4.30	$0
2009	0	0	0	0	0	0	0	$4.40	$0
TOTAL	100000	152750	112500	455625	2916000	3736875	80		$7204489

(continued)

ANNUAL REVENUES FROM SALE OF INDUSTRIAL AND CHURCH LAND

YEAR	IND. LAND ACREAGE	IND. LAND $/ACRE	IND. LAND REVENUE	PEOPLE/ CHURCH	CHURCH SITES	ACRES/ CHURCH	CHURCH ACREAGE	CHURCH LAND $	TOTAL CHURCH $
1960	0	$0	$0	3000	0	4.00	0	$0	$0
1961	0	$0	$0	3000	0	4.00	0	$0	$0
1962	0	$0	$0	3000	0	4.00	0	$0	$0
1963	0	$0	$0	3000	0	4.00	0	$0	$0
1964	0	$0	$0	3000	0	4.00	0	$0	$0
1965	0	$0	$0	3000	0	4.00	0	$0	$0
1966	0	$0	$0	3000	0	4.00	0	$0	$0
1967	0	$0	$0	3000	0	4.00	0	$0	$0
1968	0	$0	$0	3000	0	4.00	0	$0	$0
1969	0	$0	$0	3000	0	4.00	0	$0	$0
1970	0	$0	$0	3000	0	4.00	0	$0	$0
1971	15	$13000	$195000	3000	0	4.00	0	$9500	$0
1972	15	$14000	$210000	3000	0	4.00	0	$10000	$0
1973	15	$15000	$225000	3000	1	4.00	4	$10500	$42000
1974	15	$16000	$240000	3000	0	4.00	0	$11000	$0
1975	15	$17000	$255000	3000	1	4.00	4	$11500	$46000
1976	20	$18000	$360000	3000	1	4.00	4	$12000	$48000
1977	20	$19000	$380000	3000	2	4.00	8	$12500	$100000
1978	20	$20000	$400000	3000	0	4.00	0	$13000	$0
1979	20	$21000	$420000	3000	0	4.00	0	$13500	$0
1980	20	$22000	$440000	3000	1	4.00	4	$14000	$55000
1981	25	$23000	$575000	3000	1	4.00	4	$14500	$58000
1982	25	$24000	$600000	3000	1	4.00	4	$15000	$60000
1983	25	$25000	$625000	3000	1	4.00	4	$15500	$62000
1984	25	$26000	$650000	3000	1	4.00	4	$16000	$64000
1985	25	$27000	$675000	3000	2	4.00	8	$16500	$132000
1986	30	$28000	$840000	3000	1	4.00	4	$17000	$58000
1987	30	$29000	$870000	3000	2	4.00	8	$17500	$140000
1988	30	$30000	$900000	3000	1	4.00	4	$18000	$72000
1989	0	$31000	$0	3000	2	4.00	8	$18500	$148000
1990	0	$32000	$0	3000	0	4.00	0	$0	$0
1991	0	$33000	$0	3000	0	4.00	0	$0	$0
1992	0	$34000	$0	3000	0	4.00	0	$0	$0
1993	0	$35000	$0	3000	0	4.00	0	$0	$0
1994	0	$36000	$0	3000	0	4.00	0	$0	$0
1995	0	$37000	$0	3000	0	4.00	0	$0	$0
1996	0	$38000	$0	3000	0	4.00	0	$0	$0
1997	0	$39000	$0	3000	0	4.00	0	$0	$0
1998	0	$40000	$0	3000	0	4.00	0	$0	$0
1999	0	$41000	$0	3000	0	4.00	0	$0	$0
2000	0	$42000	$0	3000	0	4.00	0	$0	$0
2001	0	$43000	$0	3000	0	4.00	0	$0	$0
2002	0	$44000	$0	3000	0	4.00	0	$0	$0
2003	0	$45000	$0	3000	0	4.00	0	$0	$0
2004	0	$46000	$0	3000	0	4.00	0	$0	$0
2005	0	$47000	$0	3000	0	4.00	0	$0	$0
2006	0	$48000	$0	3000	0	4.00	0	$0	$0
2007	0	$49000	$0	3000	0	4.00	0	$0	$0
2008	0	$50000	$0	3000	0	4.00	0	$0	$0
2009	0	$51000	$0	3000	0	4.00	0	$0	$0

ANNUAL REVENUES FROM SALE OF GOLF COURSE LAND

	PEOPLE / GOLF SITE	GOLF SITES	ACRES / GOLF SITE	GOLF SITE ACREAGE	$/ACRE GOLF SITE	TOTAL GOLF SITE REVENUE
1960	25000	0	150	0	$ 0	$ 0
1961	25000	0	150	0	$ 0	$ 0
1962	25000	0	150	0	$ 0	$ 0
1963	25000	0	150	0	$ 0	$ 0
1964	25000	0	150	0	$ 0	$ 0
1965	25000	0	150	0	$ 0	$ 0
1966	25000	0	150	0	$ 0	$ 0
1967	25000	0	150	0	$ 0	$ 0
1968	25000	0	150	0	$ 0	$ 0
1969	25000	0	150	0	$ 0	$ 0
1970	25000	0	150	0	$ 0	$ 0
1971	25000	0	150	0	$3170	$ 0
1972	25000	0	150	0	$3340	$ 0
1973	25000	0	150	0	$3510	$ 0
1974	25000	0	150	0	$3680	$ 0
1975	25000	0	150	0	$3850	$ 0
1976	25000	1	150	150	$4020	$ 603000
1977	25000	0	150	0	$4190	$ 0
1978	25000	0	150	0	$4360	$ 0
1979	25000	0	150	0	$4530	$ 0
1980	25000	0	150	0	$4700	$ 0
1981	25000	0	150	0	$4870	$ 0
1982	25000	0	150	0	$5040	$ 0
1983	25000	0	150	0	$5210	$ 0
1984	25000	0	150	0	$5380	$ 0
1985	25000	1	150	150	$5550	$ 832500
1986	25000	0	150	0	$5720	$ 0
1987	25000	0	150	0	$5890	$ 0
1988	25000	0	150	0	$6060	$ 0
1989	25000	1	150	150	$6230	$ 934500
1990	25000	0	150	0	$6400	$ 0
1991	25000	0	150	0	$6570	$ 0
1992	25000	0	150	0	$6740	$ 0
1993	25000	0	150	0	$6910	$ 0
1994	25000	0	150	0	$7080	$ 0
1995	25000	0	150	0	$7250	$ 0
1996	25000	0	150	0	$7420	$ 0
1997	25000	0	150	0	$7590	$ 0
1998	25000	0	150	0	$7760	$ 0
1999	25000	0	150	0	$7930	$ 0
2000	25000	0	150	0	$8100	$ 0
2001	25000	0	150	0	$8270	$ 0
2002	25000	0	150	0	$8440	$ 0
2003	25000	0	150	0	$8610	$ 0
2004	25000	0	150	0	$8780	$ 0
2005	25000	0	150	0	$8950	$ 0
2006	25000	0	150	0	$9120	$ 0
2007	25000	0	150	0	$9290	$ 0
2008	25000	0	150	0	$9460	$ 0
2009	25000	0	150	0	$9630	$ 0
TOTAL		3		450		$2370000

(continued)

97

APPENDIX 5.1, continued

			ELEMENTARY SCHOOL LAND REQUIREMENTS						
	ANNUAL D.U.	CUMUL D.U.	STUDENTS PER D.U.	NUMBER STUDENTS	CUMUL STUDENTS	STUDENTS PER SITE	SCHOOL SITES	ACRES PER SITE	SCHOOL ACREAGE
1960	0	0	0.64	0	0	750	0	10	0
1961	0	0	0.64	0	0	750	0	10	0
1962	0	0	0.64	0	0	750	0	10	0
1963	0	0	0.64	0	0	750	0	10	0
1964	0	0	0.64	0	0	750	0	10	0
1965	0	0	0.64	0	0	750	0	10	0
1966	0	0	0.64	0	0	750	0	10	0
1967	0	0	0.64	0	0	750	0	10	0
1968	0	0	0.64	0	0	750	0	10	0
1969	0	0	0.64	0	0	750	0	10	0
1970	0	0	0.64	0	0	750	0	10	0
1971	0	0	0.64	0	0	750	0	10	0
1972	143	143	0.64	91	91	750	0	10	0
1973	146	289	0.64	93	184	750	0	10	0
1974	145	434	0.64	92	276	750	0	10	0
1975	1608	2042	0.64	1029	1305	750	1	10	10
1976	1185	3227	0.64	758	2063	750	1	10	10
1977	1138	4365	0.64	728	2791	750	1	10	10
1978	970	5335	0.64	620	3411	750	1	10	10
1979	878	6213	0.64	561	3972	750	1	10	10
1980	755	6968	0.64	483	4455	750	0	10	0
1981	669	7637	0.64	428	4883	750	1	10	10
1982	959	8596	0.64	613	5496	750	1	10	10
1983	1037	9633	0.64	663	6159	750	1	10	10
1984	1729	11362	0.64	1106	7265	750	1	10	10
1985	2039	13401	0.64	1304	8569	750	2	10	20
1986	1943	15344	0.64	1243	9812	750	1	10	10
1987	1945	17289	0.64	1244	11056	750	2	10	20
1988	2086	19375	0.64	1335	12391	750	1	10	10
1989	1958	21333	0.64	1253	13644	750	1	10	10
1990	0	21333	0.64	0	13644	750	0	10	0
1991	0	21333	0.64	0	13644	750	0	10	0
1992	0	21333	0.64	0	13644	750	0	10	0
1993	0	21333	0.64	0	13644	750	0	10	0
1994	0	21333	0.64	0	13644	750	0	10	0
1995	0	21333	0.64	0	13644	750	0	10	0
1996	0	21333	0.64	0	13644	750	0	10	0
1997	0	21333	0.64	0	13644	750	0	10	0
1998	0	21333	0.64	0	13644	750	0	10	0
1999	0	21333	0.64	0	13644	750	0	10	0
2000	0	21333	0.64	0	13644	750	0	10	0
2001	0	21333	0.64	0	13644	750	0	10	0
2002	0	21333	0.64	0	13644	750	0	10	0
2003	0	21333	0.64	0	13644	750	0	10	0
2004	0	21333	0.64	0	13644	750	0	10	0
2005	0	21333	0.64	0	13644	750	0	10	0
2006	0	21333	0.64	0	13644	750	0	10	0
2007	0	21333	0.64	0	13644	750	0	10	0
2008	0	21333	0.64	0	13644	750	0	10	0
2009	0	21333	0.64	0	13644	750	0	10	0
TOTAL	21333								

JUNIOR HIGH SCHCCL LAND REQUIREMENTS

	ANNUAL D.U.	CUMUL D.U.	STUDENTS PER D.U.	NUMBER STUDENTS	CUMJL STUDENTS	STUDENTS PER SITE	SCHOOL SITES	ACRES PER SITE	SCHOOL ACREAGE
1960	0	C	C.21	0	0	1000	0	20	0
1961	0	C	C.21	0	0	1000	0	20	0
1962	0	C	C.21	0	0	1000	0	20	0
1963	0	C	C.21	0	0	1000	0	20	0
1964	0	C	C.21	0	0	1000	0	20	0
1965	0	C	C.21	0	0	1000	0	20	0
1966	0	C	C.21	0	0	1000	0	20	0
1967	0	C	C.21	0	0	1000	0	20	0
1968	0	C	C.21	0	0	1000	0	20	0
1969	0	C	C.21	0	0	1000	0	20	0
1970	0	C	C.21	0	0	1000	0	20	0
1971	0	C	C.21	0	0	1000	0	20	0
1972	143	143	0.21	30	30	1000	0	20	0
1973	146	289	0.21	30	60	1000	0	20	0
1974	145	434	0.21	30	90	1000	0	20	0
1975	1608	2C42	C.21	337	427	1000	0	20	0
1976	1185	3227	0.21	248	675	1000	1	20	20
1977	1138	4365	0.21	238	913	1000	0	20	0
1978	970	5335	0.21	203	1116	1000	0	20	0
1979	878	6213	0.21	184	1300	1000	1	20	20
1980	755	6968	0.21	158	1458	1000	0	20	0
1981	669	7637	0.21	140	1598	1000	0	20	0
1982	959	8596	0.21	201	1799	1000	1	20	20
1983	1037	9633	0.21	217	2016	1000	0	20	0
1984	1729	11362	0.21	363	2379	1000	0	20	0
1985	2039	134C1	0.21	428	2807	1000	1	20	20
1986	1943	15344	0.21	408	3215	1000	0	20	0
1987	1945	17289	0.21	408	3623	1000	1	20	20
1988	2086	19375	0.21	438	4061	1000	0	20	0
1989	1958	21333	0.21	411	4472	1000	1	20	20
1990	0	21333	0.21	0	4472	1000	0	20	0
1991	0	21333	0.21	0	4472	1000	0	20	0
1992	0	21333	0.21	0	4472	1000	0	20	0
1993	0	21333	0.21	0	4472	1000	0	20	0
1994	0	21333	0.21	0	4472	1000	0	20	0
1995	0	21333	0.21	0	4472	1000	0	20	0
1996	0	21333	0.21	0	4472	1000	0	20	0
1997	0	21333	0.21	0	4472	1000	0	20	0
1998	0	21333	0.21	0	4472	1000	0	20	0
1999	0	21333	0.21	0	4472	1000	0	20	0
2000	0	21333	0.21	0	4472	1000	0	20	0
2001	0	21333	0.21	0	4472	1000	0	20	0
2002	0	21333	0.21	0	4472	1000	0	20	0
2003	0	21333	0.21	0	4472	1000	0	20	0
2004	0	21333	0.21	0	4472	1000	0	20	0
2005	0	21333	0.21	0	4472	1000	0	20	0
2006	0	21333	0.21	0	4472	1000	0	20	0
2007	0	21333	G.21	0	4472	1000	0	20	0
2008	0	21333	0.21	0	4472	1000	0	20	0
2009	0	21333	0.21	0	4472	1000	0	20	0
TOTAL	21333			4472			5		100

APPENDIX 5.1, continued

SENIOR HIGH SCHOOL LAND REQUIREMENTS

	ANNUAL D.U.	CUMUL D.U.	STUDENTS PER D.U.	NUMBER STUDENTS	CUMUL STUDENTS	STUDENTS PER SITE	SCHOOL SITES	ACRES PER SITE	SCHOOL ACREAGE
1960	0	0	0.16	0	0	1800	0	40	0
1961	0	0	0.16	0	0	1800	0	40	0
1962	0	0	0.16	0	0	1800	0	40	0
1963	0	0	0.16	0	0	1800	0	40	0
1964	0	0	0.16	0	0	1800	0	40	0
1965	0	0	0.16	0	0	1800	0	40	0
1966	0	0	0.16	0	0	1800	0	40	0
1967	0	0	0.16	0	0	1800	0	40	0
1968	0	0	0.16	0	0	1800	0	40	0
1969	0	0	0.16	0	0	1800	0	40	0
1970	0	0	0.16	0	0	1800	0	40	0
1971	0	0	0.16	0	0	1800	0	40	0
1972	143	143	0.16	22	22	1800	0	40	0
1973	146	289	0.16	23	45	1800	0	40	0
1974	145	434	0.16	23	68	1800	0	40	0
1975	1608	2042	0.16	257	325	1800	0	40	0
1976	1185	3227	0.16	189	514	1800	0	40	0
1977	1138	4365	0.16	182	696	1800	1	40	40
1978	970	5335	0.16	155	851	1800	0	40	0
1979	878	6213	0.16	140	991	1800	0	40	0
1980	755	6968	0.16	120	1111	1800	0	40	0
1981	669	7637	0.16	107	1218	1800	0	40	0
1982	959	8596	0.16	153	1371	1800	0	40	0
1983	1037	9633	0.16	165	1536	1800	0	40	0
1984	1729	11362	0.16	276	1812	1800	0	40	0
1985	2039	13401	0.16	326	2138	1800	0	40	0
1986	1943	15344	0.16	310	2448	1800	0	40	0
1987	1945	17289	0.16	311	2759	1800	1	40	40
1988	2086	19375	0.16	333	3092	1800	0	40	0
1989	1958	21333	0.16	313	3405	1800	0	40	0
1990	0	21333	0.16	0	3405	1800	0	40	0
1991	0	21333	0.16	0	3405	1800	0	40	0
1992	0	21333	0.16	0	3405	1800	0	40	0
1993	0	21333	0.16	0	3405	1800	0	40	0
1994	0	21333	0.16	0	3405	1800	0	40	0
1995	0	21333	0.16	0	3405	1800	0	40	0
1996	0	21333	0.16	0	3405	1800	0	40	0
1997	0	21333	0.16	0	3405	1800	0	40	0
1998	0	21333	0.16	0	3405	1800	0	40	0
1999	0	21333	0.16	0	3405	1800	0	40	0
2000	0	21333	0.16	0	3405	1800	0	40	0
2001	0	21333	0.16	0	3405	1800	0	40	0
2002	0	21333	0.16	0	3405	1800	0	40	0
2003	0	21333	0.16	0	3405	1800	0	40	0
2004	0	21333	0.16	0	3405	1800	0	40	0
2005	0	21333	0.16	0	3405	1800	0	40	0
2006	0	21333	0.16	0	3405	1800	0	40	0
2007	0	21333	0.16	0	3405	1800	0	40	0
2008	0	21333	0.16	0	3405	1800	0	40	0
2009	0	21333	0.16	0	3405	1800	0	40	0
TOTAL	21333			3405			2		80

REVENUE FROM SALE OF LAND FOR SCHOOL SITES

YEAR	SCHOOL $/ACRE	ELEM. ACREAGE	JR. HIGH ACREAGE	SR. HIGH ACREAGE	TOTAL ACREAGE	ELEM. REVENUE	JR. HIGH REVENUE	SR. HIGH REVENUE	TOTAL REVENUE
1960	$0	0	0	0	0	$0	$0	$0	$0
1961	$0	0	0	0	0	$0	$0	$0	$0
1962	$0	0	0	0	0	$0	$0	$0	$0
1963	$0	0	0	0	0	$0	$0	$0	$0
1964	$0	0	0	0	0	$0	$0	$0	$0
1965	$0	0	0	0	0	$0	$0	$0	$0
1966	$0	0	0	0	0	$0	$0	$0	$0
1967	$0	0	0	0	0	$0	$0	$0	$0
1968	$0	0	0	0	0	$0	$0	$0	$0
1969	$0	0	0	0	0	$0	$0	$0	$0
1970	$6330	0	0	0	0	$0	$0	$0	$0
1971	$6660	0	0	0	0	$0	$0	$0	$0
1972	$6990	0	0	0	0	$0	$0	$0	$0
1973	$7320	10	0	0	10	$73200	$0	$0	$73200
1974	$7650	10	20	0	30	$76500	$153000	$0	$229500
1975	$7980	10	0	0	10	$79800	$0	$0	$79800
1976	$8310	10	0	40	50	$83100	$0	$332400	$415500
1977	$8640	10	0	0	10	$86400	$0	$0	$85400
1978	$8970	0	0	0	0	$0	$0	$0	$0
1979	$9300	10	20	0	30	$93000	$186000	$0	$279000
1980	$9630	10	0	0	10	$96300	$0	$0	$96300
1981	$9960	0	0	0	0	$0	$0	$0	$0
1982	$10290	10	0	0	10	$102900	$0	$0	$102900
1983	$10620	20	0	0	20	$212400	$0	$0	$212400
1984	$10950	10	20	0	30	$109500	$219000	$0	$328500
1985	$11280	10	0	40	50	$112800	$0	$451200	$564000
1986	$11610	20	20	0	40	$232200	$232200	$0	$464400
1987	$11940	10	0	0	10	$119400	$0	$0	$119400
1988	$12270	10	20	0	30	$122700	$245400	$0	$368100
1989	$12600	0	0	0	0	$0	$0	$0	$0
1990	$12930	0	0	0	0	$0	$0	$0	$0
1991	$13260	0	0	0	0	$0	$0	$0	$0
1992	$13590	0	0	0	0	$0	$0	$0	$0
1993	$13920	0	0	0	0	$0	$0	$0	$0
1994	$14250	0	0	0	0	$0	$0	$0	$0
1995	$14580	0	0	0	0	$0	$0	$0	$0
1996	$14910	0	0	0	0	$0	$0	$0	$0
1997	$15240	0	0	0	0	$0	$0	$0	$0
1998	$15570	0	0	0	0	$0	$0	$0	$0
1999	$15900	0	0	0	0	$0	$0	$0	$0
2000	$16230	0	0	0	0	$0	$0	$0	$0
2001	$16560	0	0	0	0	$0	$0	$0	$0
2002	$16890	0	0	0	0	$0	$0	$0	$0
2003	$17220	0	0	0	0	$0	$0	$0	$0
2004	$17550	0	0	0	0	$0	$0	$0	$0
2005	$17880	0	0	0	0	$0	$0	$0	$0
2006	$18210	0	0	0	0	$0	$0	$0	$0
2007	$18540	0	0	0	0	$0	$0	$0	$0
2008	$18870	0	0	0	0	$0	$0	$0	$0
2009		0	0	0	0	$0	$0	$0	$0
TOTAL		160	100	80	340	$1600200	$1035600	$783600	$3419400

(continued)

APPENDIX 5.1, continued

SUMMARY OF LAND ACREAGE ABSORPTION

YEAR	RESID. ACREAGE	COMML ACREAGE	IND. ACREAGE	CHURCH ACREAGE	SCHOOL ACREAGE	GOLF SITE ACREAGE	TOTAL ACREAGE
1960	0	0	0	0	0	0	0
1961	0	0	0	0	0	0	0
1962	0	0	0	0	0	0	0
1963	0	0	0	0	0	0	0
1964	0	0	0	0	0	0	0
1965	0	0	0	0	0	0	0
1966	0	0	0	0	0	0	0
1967	0	0	0	0	0	0	0
1968	0	0	0	0	0	0	0
1969	0	0	0	0	0	0	0
1970	0	0	0	0	0	0	0
1971	47	0	15	0	0	0	52
1972	44	0	15	0	0	0	59
1973	44	0	15	4	0	0	63
1974	203	2	15	0	10	0	228
1975	171	0	15	0	30	0	222
1976	170	6	20	4	10	150	354
1977	146	5	20	8	50	0	230
1978	133	0	20	0	10	0	168
1979	127	1	20	4	10	0	178
1980	116	8	20	4	30	0	178
1981	154	0	25	4	10	0	193
1982	157	1	25	4	0	0	187
1983	234	6	25	4	10	0	279
1984	289	4	25	4	20	0	342
1985	271	7	25	8	30	150	491
1986	255	2	25	4	50	0	341
1987	265	11	30	8	40	0	354
1988	239	5	30	8	10	0	288
1989	0	22	30	8	30	150	210
1990	0	0	0	0	0	0	0
1991	0	0	0	0	0	0	0
1992	0	0	0	0	0	0	0
1993	0	0	0	0	0	0	0
1994	0	0	0	0	0	0	0
1995	0	0	0	0	0	0	0
1996	0	0	0	0	0	0	0
1997	0	0	0	0	0	0	0
1998	0	0	0	0	0	0	0
1999	0	0	0	0	0	0	0
2000	0	0	0	0	0	0	0
2001	0	0	0	0	0	0	0
2002	0	0	0	0	0	0	0
2003	0	0	0	0	0	0	0
2004	0	0	0	0	0	0	0
2005	0	0	0	0	0	0	0
2006	0	0	0	0	0	0	0
2007	0	0	0	0	0	0	0
2008	0	0	0	0	0	0	0
2009	0	0	0	0	0	0	0
TOTAL	3045	80	360	72	360	450	4327

SUMMARY OF REVENUE FROM SALE OF LAND - CASH BASIS

	RESID. REVENUE	COMML REVENUE	IND. REVENUE	CHURCH REVENUE	SCHOOL REVENUE	GOLF SITE REVENUE	TOTAL REVENUE
1960	0	0	0	0	0	0	0
1961	0	0	0	0	0	0	0
1962	0	0	0	0	0	0	0
1963	0	0	0	0	0	0	0
1964	0	0	0	0	0	0	0
1965	0	0	0	0	0	0	0
1966	0	0	0	0	0	0	0
1967	0	0	0	0	0	0	0
1968	0	0	0	0	0	0	0
1969	0	0	0	0	0	0	0
1970	1010500	0	195000	0	0	0	1205500
1971	982000	0	210000	0	0	0	1192000
1972	1006000	14820	225000	42000	0	0	1287820
1973	6352000	0	240000	0	73200	0	6665200
1974	5224500	114700	255000	46000	229500	0	5859700
1975	5271000	0	360000	48000	99800	603000	6361800
1976	4633000	319949	380000	100000	415500	0	5848449
1977	4316500	325324	400000	56000	8640	0	5128224
1978	4045000	77659	420000	58000	279000	0	4562699
1979	3752250	550311	440000	60000	96300	0	5077551
1980	5297000	0	575000	0	0	0	6625300
1981	5582750	125759	600000	0	0	0	6668559
1982	9235500	493873	625000	62000	102900	0	10519273
1983	11534250	334874	650000	64000	212400	0	12795524
1984	11098500	657748	675000	132000	328500	832500	13724268
1985	10916250	248639	840000	68000	564000	0	12636889
1986	11732000	1073541	870000	140000	0	0	14279941
1987	11062500	543660	900000	72000	119400	0	12697560
1988	0	2323552	0	148000	368100	934500	3774152
1989	0	0	0	0	0	0	0
1990	0	0	0	0	0	0	0
1991	0	0	0	0	0	0	0
1992	0	0	0	0	0	0	0
1993	0	0	0	0	0	0	0
1994	0	0	0	0	0	0	0
1995	0	0	0	0	0	0	0
1996	0	0	0	0	0	0	0
1997	0	0	0	0	0	0	0
1998	0	0	0	0	0	0	0
1999	0	0	0	0	0	0	0
2000	0	0	0	0	0	0	0
2001	0	0	0	0	0	0	0
2002	0	0	0	0	0	0	0
2003	0	0	0	0	0	0	0
2004	0	0	0	0	0	0	0
2005	0	0	0	0	0	0	0
2006	0	0	0	0	0	0	0
2007	0	0	0	0	0	0	0
2008	0	0	0	0	0	0	0
2009	0	0	0	0	0	0	0
TOTAL	$113151408	$ 7204489	$8860000	$1096000	$3419400	$2370000	$136101389

(continued)

103

APPENDIX 5.1, continued

LAND IMPROVEMENT - COMMUNITY DEVELOPER

	DESIGN + ENGINEERING	LANDSCAPING	ROADS	STORM SEWER	UNDERGROUND WIRING	WATER	SEWER	OTHER	TOTAL COST
1970	$ 0	$172000	$147000	$281000	$23000				$ 623000
1971	$ 1250000	$307000	$262000	$143000	$42000				$ 2004000
1972	$ 1250000	$326000	$278000	$152000	$45000				$ 2051000
1973	$ 0	$326000	$278000	$152000	$45000				$ 801000
1974	$ 0	$294000	$251000	$137000	$41000				$ 723000
1975	$ -2000000	$326000	$278000	$152000	$45000				$ -1199000
1976	$ -100000	$243000	$207000	$114000	$34000				$ 498000
1977	$ -100000	$217000	$186000	$102000	$30000				$ 435000
1978	$ -100000	$262000	$224000	$122000	$36000				$ 544000
1979	$ -100000	$275000	$235000	$128000	$38000				$ 575000
1980	$ -100000	$281000	$240000	$131000	$39000				$ 591000
1981	$ 0	$390000	$333000	$182000	$54000				$ 959000
1982	$ 0	$710000	$606000	$333000	$99000				$ 1748000
1983	$ 0	$505000	$432000	$236000	$70000				$ 1243000
1984	$ 0	$492000	$421000	$230000	$68000				$ 1211000
1985	$ 0	$518000	$443000	$243000	$72000				$ 1275000
1986	$ 0	$435000	$371000	$203000	$60000				$ 1069000
1987	$ 0	$313000	$267000	$146000	$43000				$ 769000
1988	$ 0	$ 0	$ 0	$ 0	$ 0				$ 0
1989	$ 0	$ 0	$ 0	$ 0	$ 0				$ 0
TOTAL	$ 0	$ 6392000	$ 5459000	$ 3187000	$884000				$ 15922000

NON-REFUNDABLE LAND IMPROVEMENT – SUBDIVIDER

	DESIGN + ENGINEERING	LANDSCAPING	ROADS	STORM SEWER	SEWER SYSTEM	WATER SYSTEM	UNDERGROUND WIRING	TOTAL COST
1970	$100000	$ 88501	$ 170657	$ 37929	$ 82156	$113740	$139026	$ 732009
1971	$ 0	$ 82852	$ 159764	$ 35508	$ 76912	$106480	$130152	$ 591668
1972	$250000	$ 82852	$ 159764	$ 35508	$ 76912	$106480	$130152	$ 891668
1973	$250000	$382249	$ 737093	$163821	$354844	$491260	$600474	$2979741
1974	$250000	$321153	$ 620901	$137997	$298908	$413820	$505818	$2594437
1975	$100000	$320110	$ 617270	$137190	$297160	$411400	$502860	$2385990
1976	$100000	$274918	$ 530126	$117822	$255208	$353320	$431868	$2063252
1977	$100000	$250439	$ 482923	$107331	$232484	$321860	$393414	$1888451
1978	$100000	$239141	$ 461137	$102489	$221996	$307340	$375666	$1807769
1979	$ 0	$218428	$ 421196	$ 93612	$202768	$280720	$343128	$1559852
1980	$ 0	$289982	$ 559174	$124278	$269192	$372680	$455532	$2070838
1981	$ 0	$293631	$ 570067	$126699	$274436	$379940	$464406	$2111179
1982	$ 0	$440622	$ 849654	$188838	$409032	$566280	$692172	$3146598
1983	$ 0	$544187	$1049359	$233223	$505172	$699380	$854862	$3886183
1984	$ 0	$510293	$ 984001	$218597	$473708	$655820	$801618	$3644137
1985	$ 0	$480165	$ 925905	$205785	$445740	$617100	$754290	$3428985
1986	$ 0	$498595	$ 962215	$213855	$463220	$641300	$783870	$3563455
1987	$ 0	$450037	$ 867809	$192873	$417772	$578380	$706962	$3213833
1988	$ 0	$ 0	$ 0	$ 0	$ 0	$ 0	$ 0	$ 0
1989	$ 0	$ 0	$ 0	$ 0	$ 0	$ 0	$ 0	$ 0
TOTAL	$1250000	$5771355	$11129015	$2473455	$5357620	$7417300	$9066270	$42455055

(continued)

105

APPENDIX 5.1, continued

LAND IMPROVEMENT – TRANSFER TC CCST OF SALES

	TOTAL LAND IMPROVE COSTS	TRANSFER OF C.D. COSTS	TRANSFER OF S.D. COSTS	TOTAL COST TRANSFERRED	UNABSORB LAND IMPROVE COSTS
1970	$1355009	$ 0	$ 0	$ 0	$1355009
1971	$2995668	$ 225508	$ 651177	$ 875685	$3074992
1972	$2992668	$ 213645	$ 609612	$ 823257	$5144403
1973	$3780741	$ 228129	$ 609612	$ 837741	$8087403
1974	$3272437	$ 826011	$2812530	$3638141	$7721699
1975	$3186990	$ 803885	$2369175	$3173060.	$5735629
1976	$3561262	$1281871	$2355321	$3637192	$4659699
1977	$2323451	$ 832854	$2022805	$2855659	$4127491
1978	$2351769	$ 608345	$1842692	$2451037	$4028223
1979	$2135852	$ 535523	$1759563	$2295486	$3868589
1980	$2661838	$ 644556	$1607160	$2251716	$4278711
1981	$3070179	$ 698873	$2133643	$2832516	$4516374
1982	$4494598	$ 677146	$2175208	$2852354	$6558618
1983	$5129183	$1010288	$3242030	$4252318	$7435483
1984	$4855137	$1238417	$4004045	$5242462	$7048158
1985	$4704985	$1777962	$3754659	$5532621	$6220522
1986	$4632455	$1234796	$3532981	$4767777	$6085200
1987	$3982833	$1281871	$3671530	$4953401	$5114632
1988	$ 0	$1042878	$3311304	$4354182	$ 760450
1989	$ 0	$ 760450	$ 0	$ 760450	$ 0
TOTAL	$58387055	$15922008	$42465047	$58387055	

ALLOCATION OF LAND COST

	CUM. ACREAGE PURCHASED	CUMULATIVE LAND COST	CUM. ACREAGE SOLD	SING. FAMILY LAND COST	TOWN HOUSE LAND COST	LOW RISE LAND COST	HIGH RISE LAND COST
1960	0	$0	0	$0	$0	$0	
1961	0	$0	0	$0	$0	$0	
1962	0	$0	0	$0	$0	$0	
1963	0	$0	0	$0	$0	$0	
1964	0	$0	0	$0	$0	$0	
1965	0	$0	0	$0	$0	$0	
1966	0	$0	0	$0	$0	$0	
1967	0	$350000	0	$0	$0	$0	
1968	0	$700000	0	$0	$0	$0	
1969	0	$910000	0	$0	$0	$0	
1970	7000	$910000	0	$0	$0	$0	
1971	7000	$910000	62	$67564	$3878	$0	
1972	7000	$910000	121	$61780	$4079	$0	
1973	7000	$910000	184	$63185	$0	$0	
1974	7000	$910000	412	$144555	$149771	$130381	
1975	7000	$910000	634	$141413	$127673	$80234	
1976	7000	$910000	988	$142817	$142750	$66862	
1977	7000	$910000	1218	$124497	$131785	$53490	
1978	7000	$910000	1386	$118680	$121956	$47973	
1979	7000	$910000	1534	$136398	$95078	$38981	
1980	7000	$910000	1712	$133858	$76757	$40268	
1981	7000	$910000	1905	$163009	$130715	$60443	
1982	7000	$910000	2092	$158864	$147096	$73999	
1983	7000	$910000	2371	$193064	$292053	$132387	
1984	7000	$910000	2713	$252738	$373959	$144505	
1985	7000	$910000	3204	$247723	$337252	$157092	
1986	7000	$910000	3545	$232680	$300879	$196323	
1987	7000	$910000	3899	$242608	$313348	$228467	
1988	7000	$910000	4187	$208609	$301213	$229838	
1989	7000	$910000	4397	$0	$0	$0	
1990	7000	$910000	4397	$0	$0	$0	
1991	7000	$910000	4397	$0	$0	$0	
1992	7000	$910000	4397	$0	$0	$0	
1993	7000	$910000	4397	$0	$0	$0	
1994	7000	$910000	4397	$0	$0	$0	
1995	7000	$910000	4397	$0	$0	$0	
1996	7000	$910000	4397	$0	$0	$0	
1997	7000	$910000	4397	$0	$0	$0	
1998	7000	$910000	4397	$0	$0	$0	
1999	7000	$910000	4397	$0	$0	$0	
2000	7000	$910000	4397	$0	$0	$0	
2001	7000	$910000	4397	$0	$0	$0	
2002	7000	$910000	4397	$0	$0	$0	
2003	7000	$910000	4397	$0	$0	$0	
2004	7000	$910000	4397	$0	$0	$0	
2005	7000	$910000	4397	$0	$0	$0	
2006	7000	$910000	4397	$0	$0	$0	
2007	7000	$910000	4397	$0	$0	$0	
2008	7000	$910000	4397	$0	$0	$0	
2009	7000	$910000	4397	$0	$0	$0	
TOTAL				$2834042	$3050242	$1681243	

(continued)

107

APPENDIX 5.1, continued

ALLOCATION OF LAND COST

Year	COMMERCIAL LAND COST	INDUSTRIAL LAND COST	CHURCH LAND COST	SCHOOL LAND COST	GOLF COURSE LAND COST	ABSORBED LAND COST	CUMULATIVE LAND COST	UNABSORBED LAND VALUE
1960	$0	$0	$0	$0	$0	$0	$0	$0
1961	$0	$0	$0	$0	$0	$0	$0	$0
1962	$0	$0	$0	$0	$0	$0	$0	$0
1963	$0	$0	$0	$0	$0	$0	$0	$0
1964	$0	$0	$0	$0	$0	$0	$0	$0
1965	$0	$0	$0	$0	$0	$0	$0	$0
1966	$0	$0	$0	$0	$0	$0	$0	$0
1967	$0	$0	$0	$0	$0	$0	$0	$0
1968	$0	$0	$0	$0	$0	$0	$0	$350000
1969	$0	$0	$0	$0	$0	$0	$0	$700000
1970	$0	$13038	$0	$0	$0	$0	$0	$9100000
1971	$0	$14041	$0	$0	$0	$80602	$80602	$9019398
1972	$991	$15044	$2808	$0	$0	$79699	$160301	$8939699
1973	$0	$16047	$0	$4894	$0	$86107	$246408	$8853592
1974	$7669	$17050	$3076	$15345	$0	$445648	$692056	$8407944
1975	$0	$24070	$3209	$5336	$0	$392460	$1084516	$8015484
1976	$0	$25408	$6686	$27781	$40318	$425362	$1509878	$7590122
1977	$21392	$26745	$0	$5777	$0	$391039	$1900917	$7199083
1978	$21752	$28082	$0	$18654	$0	$342883	$2243800	$6856200
1979	$5195	$29419	$3744	$6439	$0	$303734	$2547534	$6552466
1980	$36795	$38446	$3878	$6880	$0	$335495	$2883029	$6216971
1981	$0	$40117	$4012	$14201	$0	$406930	$3289959	$5810041
1982	$8411	$41789	$4145	$21964	$0	$432499	$3722458	$5377542
1983	$33021	$43460	$4279	$37710	$0	$703339	$4425797	$4674203
1984	$22390	$45132	$8826	$31051	$55663	$855532	$5281329	$3818671
1985	$43978	$56164	$4547	$7983	$0	$917630	$6198959	$2901041
1986	$16624	$58170	$4814	$24612	$0	$844927	$7043886	$2056114
1987	$71179	$60176	$9896	$0	$62482	$954784	$7998670	$1101330
1988	$36350	$0	$0	$0	$0	$848983	$8847653	$252347
1989	$155357	$0	$0	$0	$0	$252347	$9100000	$0
1990	$0	$0	$0	$0	$0	$0	$9100000	$0
1991	$0	$0	$0	$0	$0	$0	$9100000	$0
1992	$0	$0	$0	$0	$0	$0	$9100000	$0
1993	$0	$0	$0	$0	$0	$0	$9100000	$0
1994	$0	$0	$0	$0	$0	$0	$9100000	$0
1995	$0	$0	$0	$0	$0	$0	$9100000	$0
1996	$0	$0	$0	$0	$0	$0	$9100000	$0
1997	$0	$0	$0	$0	$0	$0	$9100000	$0
1998	$0	$0	$0	$0	$0	$0	$9100000	$0
1999	$0	$0	$0	$0	$0	$0	$9100000	$0
2000	$0	$0	$0	$0	$0	$0	$9100000	$0
2001	$0	$0	$0	$0	$0	$0	$9100000	$0
2002	$0	$0	$0	$0	$0	$0	$9100000	$0
2003	$0	$0	$0	$0	$0	$0	$9100000	$0
2004	$0	$0	$0	$0	$0	$0	$9100000	$0
2005	$0	$0	$0	$0	$0	$0	$9100000	$0
2006	$0	$0	$0	$0	$0	$0	$9100000	$0
2007	$0	$0	$0	$0	$0	$0	$9100000	$0
2008	$0	$0	$0	$0	$0	$0	$9100000	$0
2009	$0	$0	$0	$0	$0	$0	$9100000	$0

SALES AND INCOME SUMMARY - NO BORROWINGS

Year	LAND REVENUE + INTERIM INCOME	ABSORBED LAND COST	IMPROVEMENT COSTS	PROPERTY TAXES	COMML + ADM. INCL DEPREC.	PROFIT/LOSS BEFORE INC TAX	PROVISION FOR TAXES	NET INCOME AFTER TAXES	CUMULATIVE NET INCOME
1960	0	0	0		0	0	0	0	0
1961	0	0	0		0	0	0	0	0
1962	0	0	0		0	0	0	0	0
1963	0	0	0		0	0	0	0	0
1964	0	0	0		0	0	0	0	0
1965	0	0	0		0	0	0	0	0
1966	0	0	0		0	0	0	0	0
1967	0	0	0		0	0	0	0	0
1968	0	0	0		334000	-334000	-170339	-163661	-163661
1969	0	0	0		632000	-632000	-322319	-309681	-473342
1970	1205500	80602	875685		935000	-685787	-349751	-336036	-809378
1971	1192000	79659	823257		1246000	-956956	-488047	-468909	-1278287
1972	1287820	86107	837741		1233000	-869028	-443204	-425824	-1704111
1973	6665200	445648	3638141		763000	1818411	927389	891022	-813089
1974	5869700	392460	3173060		633000	1671180	852301	818879	5790
1975	6361800	425362	3637192		633000	1666246	849785	816461	822251
1976	5848449	391039	2855659		633000	1968751	1004062	964689	1786940
1977	5128224	342883	2451037		633000	1701304	867665	833639	2620579
1978	4542699	303734	2295486		633000	1310479	668344	642135	3262714
1979	5077561	339495	2251716		633000	1853350	945208	908142	4170856
1980	6026300	402930	2832516		608000	2182854	1113255	1069599	5240455
1981	6468549	432459	2852354		534000	2649696	1351344	1298352	6538807
1982	10519273	703339	4252318		534000	5029616	2565104	2464512	9003319
1983	12795524	855532	5242462		534000	6163530	3143400	3020130	12023449
1984	13724248	917630	5532621		534000	6739997	3437398	3302599	15326048
1985	12636889	844927	4767777		534000	6490185	3309994	3180191	18506239
1986	14279941	954784	4953401		208000	8163756	4163515	4000241	22506480
1987	12697560	848983	4354182		208000	7286395	3716061	3570334	26076814
1988	3774152	252347	760450		132000	2629355	1340971	1288384	27365198
1989	0	0	0		0	0	0	0	27365198
1990	0	0	0		0	0	0	0	27365198
1991	0	0	0		0	0	0	0	27365198
1992	0	0	0		0	0	0	0	27365198
1993	0	0	0		0	0	0	0	27365198
1994	0	0	0		0	0	0	0	27365198
1995	0	0	0		0	0	0	0	27365198
1996	0	0	0		0	0	0	0	27365198
1997	0	0	0		0	0	0	0	27365198
1998	0	0	0		0	0	0	0	27365198
1999	0	0	0		0	0	0	0	27365198
2000	0	0	0		0	0	0	0	27365198
2001	0	0	0		0	0	0	0	27365198
2002	0	0	0		0	0	0	0	27365198
2003	0	0	0		0	0	0	0	27365198
2004	0	0	0		0	0	0	0	27365198
2005	0	0	0		0	0	0	0	27365198
2006	0	0	0		0	0	0	0	27365198
2007	0	0	0		0	0	0	0	27365198
2008	0	0	0		0	0	0	0	27365198
2009	0	0	0		0	0	0	0	27365198
TOTAL	$136101389	$9100000	$58387055		$12767000	$55847334	$28482136	$27365198	

(continued)

CASH FLOW PROJECTION - NC BCRRCWING

Year	LAND REVENUE + INTERIM INCOME	LAND + INVEST	IMPROVEMENT COSTS	WORKING CAPITAL	CHANGE IN WRKNG CAPTL	COMMERCIAL + ADMIN COSTS	PROPERTY AND INCOME TAXES	CASH FLOW	CUMULATIVE CASH FLOW
1960	0	0	0	0	0	0	0	0	0
1961	0	0	0	0	0	0	0	0	0
1962	0	0	0	0	0	0	0	0	0
1963	0	0	0	0	0	0	0	0	0
1964	0	0	0	0	0	0	0	0	0
1965	0	0	0	0	0	0	0	0	0
1966	0	0	0	0	0	0	0	0	0
1967	0	350000	0	0	0	0	0	-350000	-350000
1968	0	350000	0	0	0	0	0	-563661	-913661
1969	0	8400000	0	0	0	0	0	-10089690	-11003351
1970	1205500	0	1355009	50000	50000	334000	-170339	-2081241	-13084592
1971	1192000	0	2595668	75000	25000	632000	-322319	-2456596	-15541188
1972	1265820	0	2892968	180824	105824	925000	-349751	-3297090	-18838278
1973	666520	0	2780741	178799	-2025	1226000	-488047	895767	-17942511
1974	5861800	0	3772437	193172	14373	1233000	-443204	3316734	-14625777
1975	5848449	0	3186990	999779	806607	763000	927389	2243938	-12381839
1976	4542264	0	2561262	880454	-119325	633000	852301	1964938	-10416901
1977	5077561	0	2323451	954269	73815	633000	849785	1383824	-9033077
1978	6028360	0	2151769	769257	-108034	633000	1004062	1193332	-7839745
1979	10518273	0	2135852	769233	-87829	633000	867665	757285	-7082460
1980	12795524	0	2061138	681404	80230	633000	668344	1092556	-5989904
1981	13724248	0	2061039	761634	142310	608000	945208	-377731	-6357635
1982	12636889	0	4294198	703944	66338	534000	1113255	1683378	-4684257
1983	12697941	0	4291187	972892	607608	534000	1351344	2921549	-1762708
1984	3774152	0	4855248	1577890	441438	534000	2565104	4908557	4145949
1985	0	0	4024485	2019328	139308	534000	3143400	4323543	8469392
1986	0	0	4632455	2058636	-163103	534000	3337398	5679136	14148528
1987	0	0	3982833	1895533	246457	208000	3309594	9010856	23159384
1988	0	0	0	2141990	-1338511	208000	4163515	3639692	26799075
1989	0	0	0	1904633	-566122	132000	3716061	566122	27355198
1990	0	0	0	566122	0	0	1340971	0	27355198
1991	0	0	0	0	0	0	0	0	27355198
1992	0	0	0	0	0	0	0	0	27355198
1993	0	0	0	0	0	0	0	0	27355198
1994	0	0	0	0	0	0	0	0	27355198
1995	0	0	0	0	0	0	0	0	27355198
1996	0	0	0	0	0	0	0	0	27355198
1997	0	0	0	0	0	0	0	0	27355198
1998	0	0	0	0	0	0	0	0	27355198
1999	0	0	0	0	0	0	0	0	27355198
2000	0	0	0	0	0	0	0	0	27355198
2001	0	0	0	0	0	0	0	0	27355198
2002	0	0	0	0	0	0	0	0	27355198
2003	0	0	0	0	0	0	0	0	27355198
2004	0	0	0	0	0	0	0	0	27355198
2005	0	0	0	0	0	0	0	0	27355198
2006	0	0	0	0	0	0	0	0	27355198
2007	0	0	0	0	0	0	0	0	27355198
2008	0	0	0	0	0	0	0	0	27355198
2009	0	0	0	0	0	0	0	0	27355198

PARTIAL FINANCING THROUGH BORROWINGS -SUMMARY OF BORROWINGS REPAYMENTS + INTEREST CHARGES

	LAND BORROWINGS	LAND REPAYMENTS	LAND LOAN BAL	LAND INTEREST	IMPROVE COST BORROWINGS	IMPROVE COST REPAYMENTS	IMPROVE COST LOAN BAL	IMPROVE COST INTEREST	TOTAL INTEREST
1960	$ 0	$ 0	$ 0	$ 0	$ 0	$ 0	$ 0	$ 0	$ 0
1961	$ 0	$ 0	$ 0	$ 0	$ 0	$ 0	$ 0	$ 0	$ 0
1962	$ 0	$ 0	$ 0	$ 0	$ 0	$ 0	$ 0	$ 0	$ 0
1963	$ 0	$ 0	$ 0	$ 0	$ 0	$ 0	$ 0	$ 0	$ 0
1964	$ 0	$ 0	$ 0	$ 0	$ 0	$ 0	$ 0	$ 0	$ 0
1965	$ 0	$ 0	$ 0	$ 0	$ 0	$ 0	$ 0	$ 0	$ 0
1966	$ 0	$ 0	$ 0	$ 0	$ 0	$ 0	$ 0	$ 0	$ 0
1967	$ 0	$ 0	$ 0	$ 0	$ 0	$ 0	$ 0	$ 0	$ 0
1968	$ 0	$ 0	$ 0	$ 0	$ 0	$ 0	$ 0	$ 0	$ 0
1969	$9099716	$ 0	$9099716	$ 0	$ 0	$ 0	$ 0	$ 0	$ 0
1970	$ 0	$ 100752	$8998964	$307115	$1219508	$ 0	$1219508	$ 41158	$ 348273
1971	$ 0	$ 99623	$8899341	$610830	$1547984	$ 0	$2767492	$134561	$ 745391
1972	$ 0	$ 107633	$8791708	$604067	$1862469	$ 0	$4629961	$249663	$ 853730
1973	$ 0	$ 557060	$8234648	$597072	$2648699	$ 0	$7278660	$401915	$ 998987
1974	$ 0	$ 490575	$7744073	$574639	$ 0	$ 329133	$6949527	$480201	$1054840
1975	$ 0	$ 531702	$7212371	$539281	$ 0	$1787462	$5162665	$408766	$ 948047
1976	$ 0	$ 488758	$6723573	$504779	$ 0	$ 968336	$4193729	$315758	$ 820537
1977	$ 0	$ 428603	$6294970	$470338	$ 0	$ 478987	$3714742	$266910	$ 737248
1978	$ 0	$ 376667	$5915303	$439335	$ 0	$ 89341	$3625401	$247729	$ 687104
1979	$ 0	$ 424368	$5490935	$412096	$ 369109	$ 143670	$3481731	$239865	$ 652634
1980	$ 0	$ 503662	$4987273	$384960	$ 213896	$ 0	$3850840	$247474	$ 632589
1981	$ 0	$ 540623	$4446650	$353639	$1838019	$ 0	$4064736	$267150	$ 620789
1982	$ 0	$ 879173	$3567477	$318334	$ 789178	$ 0	$5902755	$364402	$ 650796
1983	$ 0	$1069415	$2498062	$270476	$ 0	$ 348592	$6691933	$325070	$ 595546
1984	$ 0	$1147037	$1351025	$204711	$ 0	$ 744872	$6363341	$439940	$ 644651
1985	$ 0	$1056158	$ 294867	$129906	$ 0	$ 821789	$5574460	$403036	$ 532942
1986	$ 0	$ 294867	$ 0	$ 9951	$ 0	$ 873511	$4603169	$373786	$ 429334
1987	$ 0	$ 0	$ 0	$ 0	$ 0	$3918763	$ 684406	$340194	$ 350145
1988	$ 0	$ 0	$ 0	$ 0	$ 0	$ 684406	$ 0	$178455	$ 178455
1989	$ 0	$ 0	$ 0	$ 0	$ 0	$ 0	$ 0	$ 23098	$ 23098
1990	$ 0	$ 0	$ 0	$ 0	$ 0	$ 0	$ 0	$ 0	$ 0
1991	$ 0	$ 0	$ 0	$ 0	$ 0	$ 0	$ 0	$ 0	$ 0
1992	$ 0	$ 0	$ 0	$ 0	$ 0	$ 0	$ 0	$ 0	$ 0
1993	$ 0	$ 0	$ 0	$ 0	$ 0	$ 0	$ 0	$ 0	$ 0
1994	$ 0	$ 0	$ 0	$ 0	$ 0	$ 0	$ 0	$ 0	$ 0
1995	$ 0	$ 0	$ 0	$ 0	$ 0	$ 0	$ 0	$ 0	$ 0
1996	$ 0	$ 0	$ 0	$ 0	$ 0	$ 0	$ 0	$ 0	$ 0
1997	$ 0	$ 0	$ 0	$ 0	$ 0	$ 0	$ 0	$ 0	$ 0
1998	$ 0	$ 0	$ 0	$ 0	$ 0	$ 0	$ 0	$ 0	$ 0
1999	$ 0	$ 0	$ 0	$ 0	$ 0	$ 0	$ 0	$ 0	$ 0
2000	$ 0	$ 0	$ 0	$ 0	$ 0	$ 0	$ 0	$ 0	$ 0
2001	$ 0	$ 0	$ 0	$ 0	$ 0	$ 0	$ 0	$ 0	$ 0
2002	$ 0	$ 0	$ 0	$ 0	$ 0	$ 0	$ 0	$ 0	$ 0
2003	$ 0	$ 0	$ 0	$ 0	$ 0	$ 0	$ 0	$ 0	$ 0
2004	$ 0	$ 0	$ 0	$ 0	$ 0	$ 0	$ 0	$ 0	$ 0
2005	$ 0	$ 0	$ 0	$ 0	$ 0	$ 0	$ 0	$ 0	$ 0
2006	$ 0	$ 0	$ 0	$ 0	$ 0	$ 0	$ 0	$ 0	$ 0
2007	$ 0	$ 0	$ 0	$ 0	$ 0	$ 0	$ 0	$ 0	$ 0
2008	$ 0	$ 0	$ 0	$ 0	$ 0	$ 0	$ 0	$ 0	$ 0
2009	$ 0	$ 0	$ 0	$ 0	$ 0	$ 0	$ 0	$ 0	$ 0
TOTAL	$9099716	$9099716		$6787177	$10488862	$10488862		$5821131	$12608308

(continued)

111

APPENDIX 5.1, continued

SALES AND INCOME SUMMARY – PARTIALLY FINANCED THROUGH BORROWINGS

	P/L BEFORE TAXES AND INTEREST	ANNUAL INTEREST	PROFIT/LOSS BEF INC TAXES	PROVISION FOR TAXES	NET INCOME ON OPERATIONS	CUMULATIVE NET INCOME
1960	$ 0	$ 0	$ 0	$ 0	$ 0	$ 0
1961	$ 0	$ 0	$ 0	$ 0	$ 0	$ 0
1962	$ 0	$ 0	$ 0	$ 0	$ 0	$ 0
1963	$ 0	$ 0	$ 0	$ 0	$ 0	$ 0
1964	$ 0	$ 0	$ 0	$ 0	$ 0	$ 0
1965	$ 0	$ 0	$ 0	$ 0	$ 0	$ 0
1966	$ 0	$ 0	$ 0	$ 0	$ 0	$ 0
1967	$ 0	$ 0	$ 0	$ 0	$ 0	$ 0
1968	$ -334000	$ 0	$ -334000	$ -170339	$ -163661	$ -163661
1969	$ -632000	$ 348273	$ -980273	$ -499939	$ -480334	$ -643995
1970	$ -685787	$ 745351	$ -1431178	$ -729900	$ -701278	$ -1345273
1971	$ -956956	$ 853730	$ -1810686	$ -923449	$ -887237	$ -2232510
1972	$ -869028	$ 998587	$ -1866015	$ -952687	$ -915328	$ -3147838
1973	$ 1818411	$ 1054840	$ 763571	$ 389421	$ 374150	$ -2773688
1974	$ 1671180	$ 948047	$ 723133	$ 368797	$ 354336	$ -2419352
1975	$ 1666246	$ 820537	$ 845709	$ 431311	$ 414398	$ -2004954
1976	$ 1968751	$ 737248	$ 1231503	$ 628066	$ 603437	$ -1401517
1977	$ 1701304	$ 687104	$ 1014200	$ 517241	$ 496959	$ -904558
1978	$ 1310479	$ 651961	$ 658518	$ 335844	$ 322674	$ -581884
1979	$ 1853350	$ 632434	$ 1220916	$ 622667	$ 598249	$ 16365
1980	$ 2182854	$ 620789	$ 1562065	$ 796653	$ 765412	$ 781777
1981	$ 2649696	$ 654796	$ 1994900	$ 1017398	$ 977502	$ 1759279
1982	$ 5029616	$ 695546	$ 4334070	$ 2210375	$ 2123695	$ 3882974
1983	$ 6163530	$ 644651	$ 5518879	$ 2814628	$ 2704251	$ 6587225
1984	$ 6739997	$ 532942	$ 6207055	$ 3165597	$ 3041458	$ 9628683
1985	$ 6490185	$ 429334	$ 6060851	$ 3091033	$ 2969818	$ 12598501
1986	$ 8163756	$ 350145	$ 7813611	$ 3984941	$ 3828670	$ 16427171
1987	$ 7286395	$ 178455	$ 7107940	$ 3625049	$ 3482891	$ 19910062
1988	$ 2629355	$ 23098	$ 2606257	$ 1329191	$ 1277066	$ 21187128
1989	$ 0	$ 0	$ 0	$ 0	$ 0	$ 21187128
1990	$ 0	$ 0	$ 0	$ 0	$ 0	$ 21187128
1991	$ 0	$ 0	$ 0	$ 0	$ 0	$ 21187128
1992	$ 0	$ 0	$ 0	$ 0	$ 0	$ 21187128
1993	$ 0	$ 0	$ 0	$ 0	$ 0	$ 21187128
1994	$ 0	$ 0	$ 0	$ 0	$ 0	$ 21187128
1995	$ 0	$ 0	$ 0	$ 0	$ 0	$ 21187128
1996	$ 0	$ 0	$ 0	$ 0	$ 0	$ 21187128
1997	$ 0	$ 0	$ 0	$ 0	$ 0	$ 21187128
1998	$ 0	$ 0	$ 0	$ 0	$ 0	$ 21187128
1999	$ 0	$ 0	$ 0	$ 0	$ 0	$ 21187128
2000	$ 0	$ 0	$ 0	$ 0	$ 0	$ 21187128
2001	$ 0	$ 0	$ 0	$ 0	$ 0	$ 21187128
2002	$ 0	$ 0	$ 0	$ 0	$ 0	$ 21187128
2003	$ 0	$ 0	$ 0	$ 0	$ 0	$ 21187128
2004	$ 0	$ 0	$ 0	$ 0	$ 0	$ 21187128
2005	$ 0	$ 0	$ 0	$ 0	$ 0	$ 21187128
2006	$ 0	$ 0	$ 0	$ 0	$ 0	$ 21187128
2007	$ 0	$ 0	$ 0	$ 0	$ 0	$ 21187128
2008	$ 0	$ 0	$ 0	$ 0	$ 0	$ 21187128
2009	$ 0	$ 0	$ 0	$ 0	$ 0	$ 21187128
TOTAL	$55847334	$12608308	$43239026	$22051898	$21187128	

CASH FLOW PROJECTION - PARTIALLY FINANCED THROUGH BORROWINGS

Year	LAND REVENUE + INTERIM INCOME	LAND INVEST IMPROVEMENTS	WORKING CAPITAL	COMMERCIAL + ADMIN COSTS	ANNUAL INTEREST	PROPERTY AND INCOME TAXES	BORROWING/ REPAYMENT	CASH FLOW	CUMULATIVE CASH FLOW
1960	0	0	0	0	0	0	0	0	0
1961	0	0	0	0	0	0	0	0	0
1962	0	0	0	0	0	0	0	0	0
1963	0	0	0	0	0	0	0	0	0
1964	0	0	0	0	0	0	0	0	0
1965	0	0	0	0	0	0	0	0	0
1966	0	0	0	0	0	0	0	0	0
1967	0	0	0	0	0	0	0	0	0
1968	0	350000	0	0	0	0	0	-350000	-350000
1969	0	350000	50000	334000	0	-170339	0	-563661	-913661
1970	0	9755009	25000	632000	348273	-499939	10319224	58881	-854780
1971	1205500	2595668	105824	935000	745391	-729900	1447232	-999251	-1854031
1972	1192000	2892668	-2025	1246000	853730	-923449	1762846	-1112078	-2965109
1973	1287820	3780741	14373	1233000	998987	-952687	2541066	-1245528	-4211637
1974	6665200	3272437	806607	763000	1054840	389421	-886193	-507298	-4718935
1975	5865700	1186950	-119325	633000	948047	368797	-2278037	574154	-4144781
1976	6361800	2561262	73815	633000	820537	431311	-1500038	341837	-3802944
1977	5848449	2323451	-77002	633000	737248	628066	-967785	635901	-3167043
1978	5128224	2351769	-108034	633000	687104	517241	-517944	529200	-2637843
1979	4542699	2135852	-87829	633000	651961	335844	-523337	350534	-2287309
1980	5077561	2661838	80230	633000	632434	622667	-55259	392133	-1895176
1981	6026300	3070179	142310	608000	620789	796653	-289766	498603	-1396573
1982	6468549	4894598	66338	534000	654796	1017398	1297396	598815	-797758
1983	10519273	5129183	607808	534000	695546	2210375	-99995	1252566	454808
1984	12799524	4855137	341438	534000	644651	2814628	-1418007	2187663	2642471
1985	13724248	4704985	139308	534000	532942	3165597	-1891909	2755507	5397978
1986	12636889	4632455	-163103	534000	429334	3091033	-1177947	2935223	8333201
1987	14279941	3982833	246457	208000	350145	3984941	-1168378	4339187	12672388
1988	12697560	0	-237357	208000	178455	3625049	-3918763	5004650	17677038
1989	3774152	0	-1338511	132000	23098	1329191	-684406	2943968	20621006
1990	0	0	-566122	0	0	0	0	566122	21187128
1991	0	0	0	0	0	0	0	0	21187128
1992	0	0	0	0	0	0	0	0	21187128
1993	0	0	0	0	0	0	0	0	21187128
1994	0	0	0	0	0	0	0	0	21187128
1995	0	0	0	0	0	0	0	0	21187128
1996	0	0	0	0	0	0	0	0	21187128
1997	0	0	0	0	0	0	0	0	21187128
1998	0	0	0	0	0	0	0	0	21187128
1999	0	0	0	0	0	0	0	0	21187128
2000	0	0	0	0	0	0	0	0	21187128
2001	0	0	0	0	0	0	0	0	21187128
2002	0	0	0	0	0	0	0	0	21187128
2003	0	0	0	0	0	0	0	0	21187128
2004	0	0	0	0	0	0	0	0	21187128
2005	0	0	0	0	0	0	0	0	21187128
2006	0	0	0	0	0	0	0	0	21187128
2007	0	0	0	0	0	0	0	0	21187128
2008	0	0	0	0	0	0	0	0	21187128
2009	0	0	0	0	0	0	0	0	21187128
TOTAL	$136101389	$67487055		$12767000	$12608308	$22051898		$21187128	

(continued)

113

APPENDIX 5.1, continued

MEASURES OF PERFORMANCE

	DISCOUNTED RATE OF RETURN		PAYBACK PERIOD (YEARS)		AVERAGE RATE OF RETURN	
	NO BORROWINGS	BORROWINGS	NO BORROWINGS	BORROWINGS	NO BORROWINGS	BORROWINGS
1968	*****	*****				
1969	*****	*****				
1970	*****	*****				
1971	*****	*****				
1972	*****	*****				
1973	*****	*****				
1974	*****	*****				
1975	*****	*****				
1976	*****	*****				
1977	*****	*****				
1978	*****	*****				
1979	*****	*****				
1980	*****	*****				
1981	*****	*****				
1982	*****	*****				
1983	*****	1.17				
1984	*****	5.01				
1985	2.19	7.87				
1986	3.79	9.83				
1987	5.32	11.75				
1988	7.01	13.24				
1989	7.53	13.88				
1990	7.60	13.98				

6

MULTI-PERIOD MODEL

Chapter 4 presented a conceptualization of an instant city linear programming formulation of a new community. Within this formulation the various interrelationships that define the new community were delineated. In Chapter 5 the development process for a new community was described. The objective of this chapter is to incorporate the results of these chapters into a multi-period model.

The development process for a new community involves many complex relationships, not easily dealt with mathematically unless certain information is provided. For example,

1. The type housing to be considered for a particular project is not known in general.

2. The density to be considered is variable and depends on the particular project.

3. The size (expressed as number of bedrooms) of each type of dwelling unit being considered is dependent upon the type of unit.

4. The period in which land development takes place, land sales are made, and dwelling units are built is particularly unwieldy, since each involves appropriate lead times, and these vary according to the land use being considered.

Therefore, the approach taken will be to develop the functional form of the multi-period model, and in Appendix 6.1 these functionals will be redefined to obtain a solution.

Since the requirement for lead times for various phases of the land development process is mathematically unwieldly, let

e   denote a general index corresponding to the year in which there is a projected demand for each of the various types of dwelling units, ZB,

115

q   denote a general index corresponding to the year in
      which land sales are made for each of the uses for
      which a demand is projected in year e,

q'   denote a general index corresponding to the year in
      which parcels are improved for subsequent sales
      beginning in year q,

i   denote a general index whose value represents the
      density at which each of the dwelling unit types can
      be built.

Consequently, revenues will be realized in the years given by q and
development costs in the years given by q'. Also, let

t   denote the index for time, where it is understood
      that t represents the double subscripted pair of e,q
      or q,q' or the single subscript e,

U_t denote the population entering the community in year t,

ZB   denote a general variable representing each of the
      dwelling unit types (Z) with B bedrooms for which a
      demand was projected.

CONSTRAINTS THAT DEPEND ON THE PLANNED POPULATION OF THE DEVELOPMENT

From the market analysis and assumptions on capture rates,
densities, persons per dwelling unit, and the length of development,
the projected demand schedule for housing can be represented as

(6.1) $\sum_i u(ZB) \cdot (ZB)_{i,t} \leq P(ZB)_t,$

where the number of people per dwelling unit, u(ZB), is a function of
the type dwelling unit by size and tenure; and $P(ZB)_t$ is the projected
population for each of the dwelling types by year.

CONSTRAINTS THAT DEPEND ON USAGE

The amount of land required for residential development, as
previously discussed, depends on the densities chosen for development.
The land required to meet the projected demand schedule is given by

(6.2)
$$\sum_B a(ZB) \cdot (ZB)_{i,t} \leq Y(Z)_{i,t} \cdot R^T,$$

where the land used per dwelling unit, $a(ZB)$, is a function of the type dwelling unit by size and tenure; and $Y(Z)_{i,t}$ is the proportion of the total saleable land, R^T, made available and sold for dwelling units of different sizes, but the same tenure each year at a density of i per acre.

All other land requirements depend on the population entering the community in year t, U_t, and the per capita acreage requirements specified for each of the uses. Among the many requirements for land use each year are the following:

(6.3) $a(d)\ U_t \leq Y(d)_t \cdot R^T,$ for industry;

(6.4) $a(g)\ U_t \leq Y(g)_t \cdot R^T,$ for educational institutions;

(6.5) $a(c)\ U_t \leq Y(c)_t \cdot R^T,$ for commercial establishments;

(6.6) $a(p)\ U_t \leq Y(p)_t \cdot R^T,$ for municipal services;

(6.7) $a(H)\ U_t \leq Y(H)_t \cdot R^T,$ for health facilities;

(6.8) $a(F)\ U_t \leq Y(F)_t \cdot R^T,$ for recreational facilities;

(6.9) $a(\lambda)\ U_t \leq Y(\lambda)_t \cdot R^T,$ for cultural facilities;

(6.10) $a(b)\ U_t \leq Y(b)_t \cdot R^T,$ for cemetery use;

(6.11) $a(m)\ U_t \leq Y(m)_t \cdot R^T,$ for churches.

If the total saleable land is not specified originally,

(6.12) $\sum_i \sum_t Y(Z)_{i,t} + \sum_d \sum_t Y(d)_t + \sum_g \sum_t Y(g)_t$

$$+ \quad \sum_{c} \sum_{t} Y(c)_t + \sum_{p} \sum_{t} Y(p)_t + \sum_{H} \sum_{t} Y(H)_t$$

$$+ \quad \sum_{F} \sum_{t} Y(F)_t + \sum_{\lambda} \sum_{t} Y(\lambda)_t + \sum_{b} \sum_{t} Y(b)_t$$

$$+ \quad \sum_{m} \sum_{t} Y(m)_t = 1$$

permits the developer to determine the total saleable land required to satisfy the demand schedule (6.1) and other related land uses (6.3)-(6.11). Once R^T is chosen constraint (6.12) provides the mechanism by which the developer can (a) determine the value associated with the development as planned; (b) examine the effect on all other land uses when additional land is made available for a single use—the structure of the model maintains the complex interrelationships typical of new community developments; (c) determine the proportion of the total saleable land absorbed over the various uses in each year; (d) determine the potential value placed on land each year for the various uses; and (e) fix the proportion of land that is made available for a particular use in any specified year.

CONSTRAINTS THAT DEPEND ON
LAND ALLOCATION

The constraints developed thus far are the temporal extensions of the single-period instant city model developed in Chapter 4. However, several other constraint sets are suggested, the most important of which are the land allocation constraints. For a given site planners must decide how much land is to be allocated over the length of the project for each of the land uses. This decision is based in part on the results of geological and topographical studies and land ownership patterns. Once the land allocations are fixed and the demand schedule specified, parcelization of the land will not change the schedule, provided the parcelizations chosen are feasible, e.g., improved land is available for sale when required. The land allocation constraints corresponding to the land use constraints (6.2)-(6.11), respectively, are the following:

$$(6.13) \qquad\qquad \sum_{t} \sum_{B} a(ZB) \cdot (ZB)_{i,t} = D(Z)_i,$$

(6.14) $\sum\limits_{t} a(d)U_t = D(d),$

$$\vdots$$

(6.22) $\sum\limits_{t} a(m)\ U_t = D(m),$

where the right-hand side gives the land allocations for each of the types of uses for the project duration. Optimal land allocations are obtainable from solution. If it is necessary to change the land allocations, the total saleable land must remain unchanged.

PARCELIZATION CONSTRAINTS

For each land allocation constraint there are several parcelization constraints. Once a developer divides his land into parcels for improvement, his resource (land) becomes subject to two forms of taxation, i.e., as improved land if unsold and as agricultural land if unimproved. The constraints corresponding to each of the land allocations for improved land are the following:

(6.23) $\overline{D}(Z)_{i,t} + \overline{T}(Z)_{i,t-1} - \sum\limits_{B} a(ZB)\cdot(ZB)_{i,t} = \overline{T}(Z)_{i,t},$

where $\overline{D}(Z)$ denotes the size of the parcel improved and made available for sale in specified periods, t; $T(Z)_{i,t-1}$ denotes the acreage remaining from a parcel that was improved and made available for sale for Z-type dwelling units at a density of i per acre in the previous periods, t-1; $\sum\limits_{B} a(ZB)\cdot(ZB)_{i,t}$ represents the actual acreage used for Z-type dwelling units at a density of i per acre in period t; and $\overline{T}(Z)_{i,t}$ denotes the improved acreage in period t that remains unsold in this period. The remaining constraints are similarly interpreted.

(6.24) $\overline{D}(d)_t + \overline{T}(d)_{t-1} - a_d \phi_d\ ^{\theta}U_t = \overline{T}(d)_t,$

$$\vdots$$

(6.32) $\overline{D}(m)_t + \overline{T}(m)_{t-1} - \overline{\phi}a_m n_m U_t = \overline{T}(m)_t.$

For each land use the sum of the parcelizations must equal the land allocation for that use. These constraints, as well as those to follow, provide a means of weighing the benefit of delaying or accelerating improvements against paying taxes on unimproved land or improved land that remains unsold. Land that is subject to taxation as unimprove land each year from the total saleable land, R^T, available is given by

(6.33) $V_{t-1} - \{\overline{D}(Z)_{i,t} + \overline{D}(d)_t + \ldots + \overline{D}(m)_t\} = V_t$,

where V_{t-1} is the amount of land remaining unimproved as of period t-1; $\{\cdot\}$ represents the amount of land that was improved in period t; and V_t represents the quantity of land as yet unimproved by the end of period t.

PROFIT OBJECTIVE

In the instant city model the objective from the developer was profit, where the per unit profits were calculated on the basis of the aggregated land acquisition, improvement, and construction costs. In the multi-period model the development of the community is viewed as a process, and the costs cannot be aggregated. In particular, a relationship must be found between the size of a parcel and its develop- ment costs. There are two approaches to formulating an objective for this model. If a linear relationship is assumed and parcel sizes are made decision variables, the objective function becomes

$$Z = \Sigma(1-\tau) \{R_t(ZB)_{i,t} + R_t' \ a(d) \ U_t + \ldots + R_t' \cdot a(m) U_t\}$$

$$- J_t \cdot \overline{D}(Z)_{i,t} - J_t \cdot \overline{D}(d)_t - \ldots - J_t \ \overline{D}(m)_t$$

$$- T_t \ \overline{T}(Z)_{i,t} - \ldots - T_t \cdot \overline{T}(m)_t - T_t \cdot V_t,$$

where R_t is the revenue from the sale of land for housing; $(ZB)_{i,t}$ is the type housing by size and tenure to be provided each year; R_t' is the revenue from the sale of nonresidential land in each year; τ is the fraction of total land proceeds that are attributed to operating expenses (excluding property taxes); J_t is the cost of on-site improve- ments; and T_t is the combined county and town tax rate and is applied to either the assessed value of improved land that remains unsold $[T(Z)_{i,t} \ldots T(m)_t]$ or agricultural land that remains unimproved (V_t) or both.

Using this function, an optimal development schedule and con- comitant parcelization schedule that maximize profit to the developer could be found if the model allocated parcels spatially. However, this means that a parcel of fixed size would have the same improvement cost no matter where it was located on the site. It is felt that this assumption is too restrictive and does not reflect the actual relationship between parcel sizes and development costs.

REVENUE OBJECTIVE

If a linear function is not assumed, the objective becomes one of revenue maximization.

$$Z = \Sigma R_t (ZB)_{i,t} + R_t' \cdot a(d)U_t + \ldots + R_t' \cdot a(m)U_t$$

This approach conforms with the view that community development is a process. It permits optimal determination of a development schedule and a parcelization schedule using the sequential procedure illustrated in Figure 7.1

APPENDIX 6.1

A Detailed Multi-Period Model Description

Redefined constraints:

$$\text{(A.1)} \qquad \sum_{i=1}^{n} u(ZB) \cdot (ZB)_{i,q,e} \leq P(ZB)_e,$$

where $u(ZB)$ is a constant, number of people per dwelling unit, which depends on the type dwelling unit by size and tenure; ZB represents the respective dwelling units by size and tenure; i may take on any integer value from 1 to n and represents the densities being contemplated for development; q may take on a single-integer value less than, or equal to, e; e may take on any integer value corresponding to the years in which there is a projected demand for dwelling units, the maximum value must be no greater than the length of the project; $(ZB)_{i,q,e}$ represents the number of dwelling unit types at a density of i per acre that were sold in year e and are on lots purchased in year q; and $P(ZB)_e$ is the projected demand for each of the dwelling unit types in year e.

$$\text{(A.2)} \qquad \sum_{B} a(ZB) \cdot (ZB)_{i,q,e} \leq Y(Z)_{i,q} \cdot R^T,$$

where B is a finite integer value representing the number of bedrooms in each of the dwelling unit types being considered; a (ZB) is a constant acres used per dwelling unit; and $Y(Z)_{i,q}$ is the proportion of land made available and sold for dwelling units of the same tenure in year q at a density of i per acre.

$$(A.3) \qquad\qquad a_d \, \phi_d \, \overline{\theta} \, U_e \leq Y_{d,q} \cdot R^T, \qquad\qquad d=n+1,2,\ldots,d',$$

where the value of d denotes a particular type of light industry; $(a_d)^{-1}$ is the average number of employees per gross acre for type d industries; $\overline{\theta}$ is the labor participation rate—percent of population in the labor force; ϕ_d represents that fraction of the labor force which is employed in d-type industries;

$$U_e = \sum_{ZB} \sum_{i=1}^{n} u(ZB) \cdot (ZB)_{i,q,e}$$

is the population entering the community in year e—land on which the dwelling units are built was purchased in year q; and $Y_{d,q}$ is the proportion of the total saleable land, R^T, made available and sold for type d industries in period q. All Y's are similarly interpreted. Recall, for each e and type use, there is a single q. The latter is required to identify each year in which revenues are derived from land that has been made available and sold, and the former is required to identify each year in which the community becomes inhabited by residents.

$$(A.4) \qquad\qquad a_g \, \{f_g\}^{-1} \, b_g \, P^s \, U_e \leq Y_{g,q} \cdot R^T, \qquad\qquad g=d'+1,\ldots,g',$$

where the value of g denotes a particular type of educational institution; a_g is average acreage used per g-type institution; f_g is the maximum number of students per g-type institution; b_g is the fraction of projected students who will be in g-type institutions; and P^s is the number of students per capita in the county in which the site is located.

$$(A.5) \qquad j(1+f_c)M_{c,e} \, SP_c \, \{S_c\}^{-1}(1+\chi_e)U_e \leq Y_{c,q} \cdot R^T, \qquad c=g'+1,\ldots,c',$$

where c denotes a particular type of commercial establishment; j is a constant that converts acres to square feet; f_c is a fraction that, when multiplied by the land required for the structure and customer parking, gives an estimate of the land required for circulation, service, and planting; $M_{c,e}$ is the market share projected for the goods and services from c-type establishments in year e; SP_c is the per capita spending potential for c-type goods and services and is obtained by multiplying the fraction of disposable income generally spent on c-type goods and services by the disposable income and dividing this by the total number of people defined for the trading area; S_c is the expenditure required to support one square foot of sales space for type-c goods and services; and χ_e is a constant in year e, which expresses the population in the trading area, outside of the proposed development, in terms of the population in the trading area within the proposed development—if the trading area is exclusively within the development, $\chi_e = 0$.

$$(A.6) \qquad j \, r_p \left(\theta_p + f_p + \gamma_p \right) U_e \leq Y_{p,q} \cdot R^T, \qquad p=c'+1,\ldots,p',$$

where r_p is a constant that gives the square foot requirement for p-type municipal buildings on a per capita basis; the area required for parking is given by the constant γ_p, which is the square foot requirement for parking per square foot of building space; the land allotted for landscaping, walks, and so forth is given by f_p times the building space, where f_p is a specified value; and θ_p is the inverse of the F A R ratio, which is the ratio of floor area to land area.

$$(A.7) \qquad a_H \, n_H \, U_e \leq Y_{H,q} \cdot R^T, \qquad H=p'+1,\ldots,H',$$

where a_H is the acreage required per type H health facility; and n_H is the number of type H facilities required per 10,000 population.

$$(A.8) \qquad a_F \, U_e \leq Y_{F,q} \cdot R^T, \qquad F=H'+1,\ldots,F',$$

where a_F is the acreage required for a type F facility (public parks and recreational areas) per 1,000 population.

$$(A.9) \qquad a_\lambda \, n_\lambda \, U_e \leq Y_{\lambda,q} \cdot R^T, \qquad \lambda=F'+1,\ldots,\lambda',$$

where a_λ is the acreage required per type λ cultural facility; and n_λ is the number of type λ facilities per 1,000 population.

$$(A.10) \qquad a_b \, U_e \leq Y_{b,q} \cdot R^T, \qquad b=\lambda'+1,\ldots,b',$$

where a_b is the acreage required for cemeteries per 1,000 population.

$$(A.11) \qquad \bar{\phi} \, a_m \, n_m \, U_e \le Y_{m,q} \cdot R^T, \qquad m=b'+1,\ldots,m',$$

where a_m is the acreage required per church; n_m is the number of churches required per capita; and $\bar{\phi}$ is the proportion of the population to be served by churches.

$$(A.12) \qquad \sum_q \sum_{i=1}^{n} Y(Z)_{i,q} + \sum_{d=n+1}^{d'} \sum_q Y_{d,q} + \sum_{g=d'+1}^{g'} \sum_q Y_{g,q}$$

$$+ \sum_{c=g'+1}^{c'} \sum_q Y_{c,q} + \sum_{p=c'+1}^{p'} \sum_q Y_{p,q} + \sum_{H=p'+1}^{H'} \sum_q Y_{H,q}$$

$$+ \sum_{F=H'+1}^{F'} \sum_q Y_{F,q} + \sum_{\lambda=F'+1}^{\lambda'} \sum_q Y_{\lambda,q} + \sum_{b=\lambda'+1}^{b'} \sum_q Y_{b,q}$$

$$+ \sum_{m=b'+1}^{m'} Y_{m,q} = 1.$$

$$(A.13) \qquad \sum_e \sum_B a(ZB) \cdot (ZB)_{i,q,e} = D(Z)_i, \qquad\qquad i=1,\ldots,n.$$

$$(A.14) \qquad \sum_e a_d \, \phi_d \, \bar{\theta} \, U_e = D_d, \qquad\qquad d=n+1,\ldots,d'.$$

$$(A.15) \qquad \sum_e a_g \, \{f_g\}^{-1} \, b_g \, P^S \, U_e = D_g, \qquad\qquad g=d'+1,\ldots,g'.$$

$$(A.16) \qquad \sum_e j(1+f_c) \, M_{c,e} \, SP_c \, \{S_c\}^{-1} \, (1+\chi_e) \, U_e = D_c, \qquad c=g'+1,\ldots,c'.$$

$$(A.17) \qquad \sum_e j \, r_p \, (\theta_p+f_p+\gamma_p) \, U_e = D_p, \qquad\qquad p=c'+1,\ldots,p'.$$

$$(A.18) \qquad \sum_e a_H \, n_H \, U_e = D_H, \qquad\qquad H=p'+1,\ldots,H'.$$

$$(A.19) \qquad \sum_e a_F \, U_e = D_F, \qquad\qquad F=H'+1,\ldots,F'.$$

$$(A.20) \quad \sum_e a_\lambda \, n_\lambda \, U_e = D_\lambda, \qquad\qquad \lambda = F'+1, \ldots, \lambda'.$$

$$(A.21) \quad \sum_e a_b \, U_e = D_b, \qquad\qquad b = \lambda'+1, \ldots, b'.$$

$$(A.22) \quad \sum_e \bar{\phi} \, a_m \, n_m \, U_e = D_m, \qquad\qquad m = b'+1, \ldots, m'.$$

$$(A.23) \quad \overline{D}(Z)_{i,q',q} + \overline{T}(Z)_{i,q'-1,q-1} - \sum_B a(ZB) \cdot (ZB)_{i,q,e}$$

$$= \overline{T}(Z)_{i,q',q,} \qquad\qquad i = 1, \ldots, n,$$

where q' may take on any integer value less than, or equal to, q; $\overline{D}(Z)_{i,q',q}$ is the parcel size improved in year q' for subsequent sale as improved building lots in year $q-Z$-type dwelling units will be constructed at a density of i per acre; $\overline{T}(Z)_{i,q'-1,q-1}$ is land that is available for sale in this period, as a result of not having been sold in the previous period—if $\overline{D}(Z)_{i,q',q}$ is the first parcel to be improved, then $\overline{T}(Z)_{i,q'-1,q-1} = 0$; $\sum_B a(ZB) \cdot (ZB)_{i,q,e}$ is the actual improved acreage sold in year q for subsequent construction of Z-type dwelling units at a density of i per acre in year e; and $\overline{T}(Z)_{i,q',q}$ represents the land that was improved in year q', but was not sold in year q and is therefore available for sale in year $q+1$—if $\overline{D}(Z)_{i,q',q}$ is the last parcel in the land allocation to be improved, then $\overline{T}(Z)_{i,q',q} = 0$. The remaining parcelization constraints for improved land are interpreted in a similar manner and are as follows:

$$(A.24) \quad \overline{D}_{d,q',q} + \overline{T}_{d,q'-1,q-1} - a_d \, \phi_d \, \bar{\theta} \, U_e$$

$$= \overline{T}_{d,q',q}, \qquad\qquad d = n+1, \ldots, d';$$

$$(A.25) \quad \overline{D}_{g,q',q} + \overline{T}_{g,q'-1,\, q-1} \, a_g \, \{f_g\}^{-1} \, b_g \, P^s \, U_e$$

$$= \overline{T}_{g,q',q}, \qquad\qquad g = d'+1, \ldots, g';$$

$$(A.26) \quad \overline{D}_{c,q',q} + \overline{T}_{c,q'-1,q-1} - j(1+f_c) \, M_{c,e} \, SP_c \, \{S_c\}^{-1}$$

$$(1+\chi_e) \, U_e = \overline{T}_{c,q',q}, \qquad\qquad c = g'+1, \ldots, c';$$

$$(A.27) \quad \overline{D}_{p,q',q} + \overline{T}_{p,q'-1,q-1} - j \ r_p \ (\theta_p + f_p + \gamma_p) \ U_e$$

$$= \overline{T}_{p,q',q'} \qquad\qquad\qquad\qquad p = c'+1, \ldots, p';$$

$$(A.28) \quad \overline{D}_{H,q',q} + \overline{T}_{H,q'-1,q-1} - a_H \ n_H \ U_e$$

$$= \overline{T}_{H,q',q'} \qquad\qquad\qquad\qquad H = p'+1, \ldots, H';$$

$$(A.29) \quad \overline{D}_{F,q',q} + \overline{T}_{F,q'-1,q-1} - a_F \ U_e$$

$$= \overline{T}_{F,q',q'} \qquad\qquad\qquad\qquad F = H'+1, \ldots, F';$$

$$(A.30) \quad \overline{D}_{\lambda,a',q} + \overline{T}_{\lambda,q'-1,q-1} - a_\lambda \ n_\lambda \ U_e$$

$$= \overline{T}_{\lambda,q',q'} \qquad\qquad\qquad\qquad \lambda = F'+1, \ldots, \lambda';$$

$$(A.31) \quad \overline{D}_{b,q',q} + \overline{T}_{b,q'-1,q-1} - a_b \ U_e$$

$$= \overline{T}_{b,q',q'} \qquad\qquad\qquad\qquad b = \lambda'+1, \ldots, b';$$

$$(A.32) \quad \overline{D}_{m,q',q} + \overline{T}_{m,q'-1,q-1} - \overline{\phi} \ a_m \ n_m \ U_e$$

$$= \overline{T}_{m,q',q'} \qquad\qquad\qquad\qquad m = b'+1, \ldots, m'.$$

For unimproved land the constraints are as follows:

$$(A.33) \quad V_{q'-1} - \left\{ \sum_{i=1}^{n} \overline{D}(Z)_{i,q',q} + \sum_{d=n+1}^{d'} \overline{D}_{d,q',q} \right.$$

$$\left. +\ldots+ \sum_{m=b'+1}^{m'} \overline{D}_{m,q',q} \right\} = V_{q'},$$

where $V_{q'-1}$ is the land remaining out of R^T that was not improved in the previous period—for the very first parcel(s) to be improved, $V_{q'-1} = R^T$; $\{\ \}$ represents the total amount of land that is improved in year q'; and $V_{q'}$ represents that quantity of land from R^T that as of year q' has not been improved— for the very last parcel to be improved, $V_{q'} = 0$.

Redefined profit objective:

$$Z = (1-\tau) \left\{ \sum_q \sum_B \sum_{i=1}^{n} L_{i,q}^{ZB} \cdot (ZB)_{i,q,e} + K_o \sum_e U_e \right\}$$

$$- \sum_{q'} \sum_{i=1}^{n} J(\overline{D}(Z))_{q'} \; F(\overline{D}(Z))\overline{D}(Z)_{i,q',q}$$

$$- \sum_{q'} K_{q'} - \sum_q \sum_{i=1}^{n} T_q E_q^r M_q T(Z)_{i,q',q} - \sum_q T_q E_q^r M_q K_q$$

$$- \sum_{q'} T_{q'} E_{q'}^r N_{q'} V_{q'},$$

where

$$K_o = j \; \bar{\theta} \sum_{d=n+1}^{d'} L_d a_d \phi_d + P^S \sum_{g=d'+1}^{g'} L_g a_g \{f_g\}^{-1} b_g +$$

$$j \sum_{c=g'+1}^{c'} L_c \{d_c^P\}^{-1} (1+f_c) M_{c,e} SP_c \{S_c\}^{-1} (1+\chi_e)$$

$$+ j \sum_{p=c'+1}^{p'} L_p r_p (\theta_p + f_p + \gamma_p)$$

$$+ \sum_{H=p'+1}^{H'} L_H a_H n_H + \sum_{F=H'+1}^{F'} L_F a_F + \sum_{\lambda=F'+1}^{\lambda'} L_\lambda a_\lambda n_\lambda$$

$$+ \sum_{b=\lambda'+1}^{b'} L_b a_b + \bar{\phi} \sum_{m=b'+1}^{m'} L_m a_m n_m;$$

$$K_{q'} = \sum_{d=n+1}^{d'} J(\overline{D}_d)_{q'} \; F(\overline{D}_d) \; \overline{D}_{d,q',q} + \sum_{g=d'+1}^{g'} J(\overline{D}_g)_{q'}$$

$$F(\overline{D}_g)\overline{D}_{g,q',q} + \ldots + \sum_{m=b'+1}^{m'} J(\overline{D}_m)_{q'} \; F(\overline{D}_m)\overline{D}_{m,q',q};$$

$$K_q = \sum_{d=n+1}^{d'} \overline{T}_{d,q',q} + \sum_{g=d'+1}^{g'} \overline{T}_{g,q',q} + \ldots + \sum_{m=b'+1}^{m'} \overline{T}_{m,q',q};$$

and

d_c^P = depth of lot to be used for c-type land use,

L_d = revenue in dollars per square foot from the sale of industrial land,

L_g = revenue in dollars per acre from the sale of land for school use,

L_c = revenue in dollars per front-foot from the sale of commercial land,

L_p = revenue in dollars per square foot from the sale of land for municipal services,

L_H = revenue in dollars per acre from the sale of land for health facilities,

L_F = revenue in dollars per acre from the sale of land for public and recreational use,

L_λ = revenue in dollars per acre from the sale of land for cultural facilities,

L_b = revenue in dollars per acre from the sale of land for cemetery use,

L_m = revenue in dollars per acre from the sale of land for churches,

L_i^{ZB} = revenue in dollars per unit from the sale of land for ZB-type dwelling units at a density of i per acre,

τ = proportion of gross sales that are considered operating expenses,

T_q = the combined town and county tax rates (dollars per 1,000 assessed valuation) prevailing in year q,

T_q' = the combined town and county tax rates prevailing in year q',

E_q = county equalization rate prevailing in year q,

$E_{q'}^r$ = county equalization rate prevailing in year q',

M_q = market value (sales price) of improved land in year q,

$N_{q'}$ = market value of unimproved land in year q',

J = cost per lineal foot of street—this is dependent on the type and size of parcel,

F = number of lineal feet per acre—this is dependent on the type and size of parcel.

Redefined revenue objective:

$$Z = \sum_q \sum_B \sum_{i=1}^{n} L_{i,q}^{ZB} \cdot (ZB)_{i,q,e} + K_o \sum_e U_e,$$

where all variables and parameters are defined as for the profit objective.

THE ROLE OF
LINEAR PROGRAMMING
IN THE LAND DEVELOPMENT
PROCESS

Utilization of the multi-period model for new community development yields significant insights into the land development process; the purpose of this chapter is to describe its contribution as a guide for decision making.

To begin the land development process, it is necessary to arrive at a market forecast and the type of environment to be provided in terms of alternative land uses, i.e., constraint sets (6.1) and (6.2)-(6.11). The maximum amount of saleable land should be estimated and incorporated into the land use constraints, R^T. The sale price for land by use is then determined. For uses other than residential information on the most recent land transactions in the region are obtained, and land sale prices are estimated. These values are incorporated into the objective function. Sale prices for residential land are obtained by estimating the market prices of dwelling types in the region comparable to those planned for in the development schedule. Land value is based on the sale price of the dwelling; real estate conditions in the region stipulate what proportion of the sale price is the land value. These estimated land sale prices—expressed on a per dwelling unit basis—are also incorporated into the objective function.

With this information and constraints (6.1)-(6.22), revenues can be maximized. The extent to which R^T is underutilized or scarce, i.e., there is not enough land to meet the demand (6.1), is determined by the optimization; also, this operation yields the best land allocations for each land use by the optimization. A decision can then be made on its acceptability as originally planned. If it is unsatisfactory a new estimate is obtained, and the problem is resolved. This cycle is continued until an acceptable amount of saleable land is found. Once established the land use allocations desired by planners (usually based on environmental design considerations, such as geology and topology) can be compared to those allocations given by the model. If different these land allocations are imposed as equality constraints, (6.13)-(6.22), and the problem is resolved. Two possibilities may result: (a) the problem remains feasible, i.e., all the constraints are satisfied, in which case we have a measure of the cost of deviating from the optimal plan; and (b) the problem is infeasible, in which case two alternatives exist: (1) amount of land in the infeasible allocation constraints can be decreased to that level required for feasibility (the level in question is known from the infeasible solution), or (2) if possible the land can be reallocated (the degree to which land must be reallocated is known from the infeasible solution).

Once the land allocations of land uses are chosen, the demand schedule will remain feasible and the revenues from development will have been determined, providing feasible parcelizations are chosen. Therefore, it is appropriate during this step in the land development process to study different types of environmental designs (alternative land uses) by considering various land allocations and noting the affect on revenue.

After establishing land use allocations decisions must be made on the sizes and timing of parcels for each of the various land uses. These decisions are based, in part, on builder requirements and zoning restrictions. The feasibility of the parcelizations is readily determined, using the optimal solution corresponding to the given land use allocations. From the optimal solution parcel sizes for the time periods specified by the developer are heuristically determined. The following rules are suggested for determining feasibility for each parcelization: (a) the chosen parcel size plus any excess land resulting from a previous parcelization must be greater than, or equal to, the optimal parcel size, unless (1) it is the first parcel, in which case there will be no excess from a previous parcel—then the chosen parcel must be greater than, or equal to, the optimal parcel size; or (2) it is the last parcel, in which case no excess can be carried forward—then the actual parcel size plus any from the previous parcel must equal the optimal parcel size.

Parts (1) and (2) can be determined by observation, and if either is violated the parcels are infeasible as chosen, i.e., dwelling units are being constructed on land that has not as yet been purchased.

If these conditions are not met, the optimal parcelizations can be used as a guide in choosing feasible parcels or different timings on parcelizations can be explored, in which case the previously discussed procedure must be begun anew. Once the chosen parcelizations are fixed, it is necessary to impose these parcels (size and timing) as constraints (6.23)-(6.32), and the problem is resolved. The solution will yield the maximum revenue (the cost of imposing these constraints will also be known), optimal development schedule, parcelization

schedule, land allocations, and the amount of land subject to taxation
as improved and unimproved land each year.

Development costs have not been explicitly considered in
determining the best plan for development. However, costs were
implicitly included in arriving at the sale prices for the various land
uses. It remains, therefore, to ensure that the actual costs of
development are not different than the costs implicit in the estimated
land sale prices. The discussion to follow will use the land development process flow chart—Figure 7.1 as a reference.

LAND DEVELOPMENT PROCESS FLOW CHART

Blocks 1-5

The preceding material in this chapter discussed the inputs
needed to use linear programming as an aid in the land development
process. How linear programming is used to arrive at the development plan that maximizes revenue was then described.

Blocks 6-10

These steps represent the calculation of the market price of
the dwelling unit. This market price is based on construction costs
and land development costs, which consists of (a) land acquisition,
(b) site improvements (off-site and on-site), and (c) operating expenses
and profit (including real estate taxes). These costs are derived from
the sketch plan, which translates the development plan, block 5, into
a spatial plan for development.

Blocks 11-16

The market price computed for the dwelling unit must be compared to the market value determined by the income distribution of
the prospective residents, subject to the opinion of realtors, bankers,
and consultants who have examined the sketch plan. If the price
exceeds the market value, it will be necessary to reevaluate the land
development costs for possible reductions or to consider a more
economical spatial plan for development. If neither is possible it
will be necessary to change the parcel sizes and, possibly, the land
use allocations. Previous experimentation should be of assistance in
determining the advisability of such changes.

FIGURE 7.1

Land Development Process Flow Chart

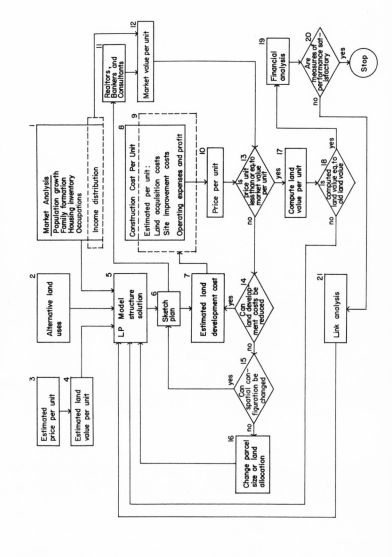

132

Blocks 17-18

Land value is based on the price of the dwelling; real estate
conditions in the region will stipulate what percentage of the market
price of the dwelling is the price of the land. If this is the first
iteration, the computed land value must be compared to the estimated
land value (block 4); otherwise, it is compared to the previously
computed land value. Equal land values verify that the actual costs
do not exceed the costs implicit in the previously chosen land value
(i.e., sale prices for the various land uses used in determining the
development plan are valid), and the financial analysis for this plan
can be performed. If the land values are unequal, the implicit cost
is different from the actual cost, and the development plan is not
valid; it is necessary to resolve the model using the new land values,
i.e., those determined by using the actual development costs.

Blocks 19-21

The financial analysis conducted is analogous to that discussed
in Chapter 5. If the measures of performance obtained from this
analysis are deemed acceptable, the analysis is complete. Otherwise,
the development plan must be modified until the results are considered
acceptable. The purpose of the link analysis is to utilize the knowledge
gained in determining the previous development plan in arriving at a
new development plan. The link analysis is the subject of Chapter 8.

The purpose of this chapter is to propose a method of linking the financial analysis to the plan for development. This linkage will help ensure that the information compiled in performing the analysis necessary in arriving at the development plan can be utilized effectively in arriving at a new development plan should the financial analysis be unsatisfactory. There are no known analytic approaches that accomplish this objective. Too often, plans that result in an unsatisfactory financial analysis are discarded and new assumptions on capture rates and project duration are invoked without careful evaluation of the present development plan. The result is the tedious calculations illustrated in the land value flow chart (Figure 5.2), or the land development process flow chart (Figure 7.1) must be begun anew. It is proposed that, before making drastic changes, such as modifying the duration of the project or the demand schedule, an attempt should be made to identify those land uses in the plan that do not yield adequate revenues upon sale. Once identified, the reallocation of these uses to land uses that do result in adequate sales revenues should be considered. Such a reallocation, however, does not guarantee a satisfactory financial analysis, but the identification of the inefficient land uses—measured by the revenue received upon sale—does permit more detailed analyses of a financially unsatisfactory development plan than presently exist.

The link analysis was developed to provide guidance in identifying those land uses that are being inefficiently utilized in a development plan. This approach is based upon the methodology presented herein and was evaluated in the case study of the Highlands project. Although it requires further study it can provide guidance in the decision-making process during the planning stages for a large-scale development.

The revenue derived from the sale of land for a specified use in a particular year is defined as satisfactory if the proportion of land sold is no greater than the proportion of revenue derived from its sale. This comparison—illustrated in the case study, Chapter 9, Table 9.10—is the basis for determining the efficient or inefficient use of land. Using this criteria, the land identified as inefficiently utilized (circled value in Table 9.10) would be reallocated to a more efficient land use (blocked value in Table 9.10). The procedure requires constraining the appropriate Y's, decision variables, and resolving the LP model. Violation of any of the constraints previously imposed—demand schedule, parcelization constraints, land allocation constraints—would be readily determined. An infeasible solution would provide guidance to the developer by specifying the nature of the assumptions required to implement the reallocation. A feasible and optimal solution would be translated into a sketch plan, and, depending on the relationship of the old land value to the computed land value, the financial analysis would be performed and the model would be resolved, using the computed land value.

Additional guidance is possible by taking advantage of the structure of the LP model. The comparison presented thus far does not yield any information on the level of usage of the land by particular use for a period, e.g., how much (relatively) was land in 1975 used for two-per-acre single-family detached dwelling units? It is felt that, by identifying the relative level of usage of land uses, the developer can better analyze the present (albeit unsatisfactory) development prior to changing assumptions on project duration or the demand schedule.

The determination of relative land use is made by utilizing indicators derived from the dual variables in the LP solution. In the multi-period model, as in the case of the instant city model, the dual variables corresponding to the land use constraints are identical and have the value u^*. However, in the multi-period model the dual variables represent the increase in revenue to be derived from making one additional acre of land available without regard to a particular use. The actual proportion of land used for a particular use v in period t is given by $Y_{v,t}$. Therefore, the value of one additional acre made available for use v in period t is given by $u^*/Y_{v,t}$. The proportion of the total market value attributed to each use is $u^*/Y_{v,t} \div \sum_{v,t} u^*/Y_{v,t}$. These proportions are the values reported in Table 9.10 and can be employed as indicators of extensive or minimal land use. If the actual proportion of land use is minimal, $Y_{v,t}$ will be less than $u^*/Y_{v,t} \div \sum_{v,t} u^*/Y_{v,t}$, and vice versa. Land is therefore defined as extensively used if the value of this indicator (and given for the case study in Table 9.10, under "proportion of cost allocated to") is less than the actual proportion of land used; if it is greater than this proportion, it is defined to be minimally used.

Four cases are of particular interest in analyzing the development plan. The decision rule for each is as follows:

Case	Proportion of Land Employed for Use v in Year t	Proportion of Costs Allocated to Use v in Year t	Proportion of Revenue Derived from the Sale of Land for Use v in Year t	Decision Rule
1	Lo	Hi	Satisfactory	Make more land available for this use
2	Lo	Hi	Unsatisfactory	Make this land available for a more efficient use
3	HI	Lo	Unsatisfactory	Make this land available for a more efficient use
4	Hi	Lo	Satisfactory	Maintain same land uses

In Table 9.10 these indicators are entitled "proportion of cost allocated to," when, in fact, they were designed as indicators for linking the financial analysis to the plan for development. However, allocating costs for management accounting on the basis of these indicators can be rationalized as follows:

1. The market value of a particular land use is given by $u*/Y_{v,t}$.
2. The market value basis for allocating costs (discussed in Chapter 5) provides that costs be allocated in the same proportion as the market value for each use, i.e., $u*/Y_{v,t} \div \sum_{v,t} u*/Y_{v,t}$.
3. Allocating the total costs (TC) on this basis yields $(u*/Y_{v,t} \div \sum_{v,t} u*/Y_{v,t}) \times TC$ for each use v and year t.

    4. The proportion of costs allocated to use v in year
t is $TC_{v,t} \div TC$ and is the indicator $u*/Y_{v,t} \div \sum\limits_{v,t} u*/Y_{v,t}$.

In the case study—Chapter 9—costs were allocated in two ways: (a)
using market value as a basis, and (b) the indicators based on the
dual variables. The internal rates of return obtained were 14 percent
and 13.38 percent, respectively.

    It must be noted that the approach presented is based upon the
dual variables, $u*$, which, due to the structure of the model, are equal.
Therefore, the value of indicators does not depend upon the duals;
the reason(s) for this result and the possibility that the proposed
link analysis can be performed independently of the LP structure of
the problem are subjects for further inquiry.

AN APPLICATION OF
THE MULTI-PERIOD
MODEL:
A CASE STUDY OF
THE HIGHLANDS PROJECT

The purpose of this chapter is to illustrate the application of the multi-period model by reference to an actual planning study—the Highlands project. Since the study was completed before the model was fully developed, the full capability of employing the model through-out the planning process for a large-scale development cannot be demonstrated.

The Highlands project is a case where a historic landowner wished to determine the feasibility of developing its holdings. The site consists of approximately 1,760 acres, over a half of which is owned by a single owner. It abuts the Hudson River and is in the center of the capital district region (Albany, Rensselaer, Saratoga, and Schenectady counties, New York). The site is situated directly across from an extensive redevelopment project, which will house the state government. Of the total acreage 130 acres is river front land, 915 acres is slope land, and 715 acres is a flatter uplands area. Only the 715 acres was considered developable.

Based on the market analysis the project staff projected a population increase of 135,470 people, or 66,100 households, for the capital district region between 1970 and 1990. This projection was refined to give housing demand by tenure (renters versus owners), persons per households, and income levels as shown in Table 9.1. Next, the fraction of this growth that could realistically be expected to occur in Rensselaer County was estimated. The Highlands staff, consultants, and concerned state agencies projected that Rensselaer County, with its direct access to employment opportunities, could capture from 30 to 35 percent of the regional growth in the 1970's and as high as 35 to 40 percent in the 1980's. Using these capture rates growth in the region and county was estimated to be as follows:

TABLE 9.1

Regional Housing Projection, 1970-90
(a)
1970-80

Tenure and Income	Persons Per Household					Total
	1	2	3	4	5	
Owner:						
Under - $3,000	$ 70	$ 180	$ 90	$ 120	$ 230	$ 690
3,000 - 4,999	110	260	140	180	340	1,030
5,000 - 6,999	180	440	230	290	570	1,710
7,000 - 9,999	380	960	500	650	1,240	3,730
10,000 - 11,999	260	650	340	440	840	2,530
12,000 - 14,999	290	700	360	470	910	2,730
15,000 - 24,999	290	710	370	480	920	2,770
25,000 - 49,999	70	160	80	110	210	630
50,000 and over	10	20	10	10	30	80
Total	1,660	4,080	2,120	2,750	5,290	15,900
Renter:						
Under - $3,000	410	310	280	440	400	1,840
3,000 - $4,499	600	450	400	640	580	2,670
5,000 - 6,999	520	390	350	550	510	2,320
7,000 - 9,999	690	530	470	730	690	3,090
10,000 - 11,999	360	260	240	370	340	1,570
12,000 - 14,999	330	250	220	350	320	1,470
15,000 - 24,999	320	240	210	340	310	1,420
25,000 - 49,999	50	30	30	50	40	200
50,000 and over	—	—	—	—	—	—
Total	$3,280	$2,460	$2,200	$3,470	$3,190	$14,600

(b)
1980-90

Tenure and Income	1	2	3	4	5	Total
Owner:						
Under - $3,000	$ 60	$ 90	$ 80	$ 200	$ 530	960
3,000 - 4,999	80	130	120	290	770	1,390
5,000 - 6,999	140	220	200	480	1,290	2,330
7,000 - 9,999	290	480	450	1,070	2,800	5,090
10,000 - 11,999	200	330	290	720	1,900	3,440
12,000 - 14,999	220	350	320	780	2,060	3,730
15,000 - 24,999	220	360	330	790	2,080	3,780
25,000 -· 49,999	50	80	80	180	460	870
50,000 and over	10	10	10	20	60	110
Total	1,270	2,050	1,880	4,530	11,970	21,700
Renter:						
Under - $3,000	370	260	180	470	470	1,750
3,000 - 4,999	540	370	270	680	680	2,540
5,000 - 6,999	470	320	230	590	590	2,200
7,000 - 9,999	630	440	300	810	820	3,000
10,000 - 11,999	310	220	160	400	400	1,490
12,000 - 14,999	290	200	150	370	370	1,380
15,000 - 24,999	290	200	140	360	360	1,350
25,000 - 49,999	40	30	20	50	50	190
50,000 and over	—	—	—	—	—	—
Total	$2,940	$2,040	$1,450	$3,730	$3,740	$13,900

139

Households	1970-80	1980-90	1970-90
Capital district (region)	30,500	35,600	66,100
Rensselaer County:			
Share	9,900	13,350	23,400
Percent	32.5	37.5	—

No development was planned for the Highlands site until 1974—the anticipated completion date of the county sewer plant. It was projected that the site could capture 30 percent of the county growth between 1974 and 1983, for a total capture of 13,700 people. The general character of the projected population and housing mix over the ten-year period is presented in Tables 9.2-9.4 in terms of the following:

    1. Households to be accommodated, by income, price (or rent) of unit, and number of bedrooms,
    2. Households by size, age of head, number of children, and number in labor force,
    3. Mix of units by size and tenure, respectively.

Per annum population projections were made for dwelling units by size and tenure. These projections, presented in Table 9.5, are based upon assumptions made by the Highlands staff on the absorption rate that would be required to make the project a feasible undertaking. Table 9.3 gives the number of households by age of head of household having one or more school-age children. In Table 9.5 the actual number of school-age children who can be expected on the site as the population grows in accordance with the demand schedule is shown—and was estimated using the 1970 census figure of .222 students per capita for Rensselaer County.

    The need for related activities, such as schools, community facilities, industries, commercial services, and so forth, was recognized in the Highlands project. However, the timing and land requirements for each of these uses was estimated and fixed by the Highlands staff. As a consequence, no direct relationship exists between population growth and the need for schools, commercial services, industrial employment, and community facilities.

    A demand was projected for residential development for three dwelling unit types:

    1. Single-family detached—one house per lot,
    2. Single-family attached—also called a "court house," "town house," "row house," or "patio house",

TABLE 9.2

Projected Housing Demand for the Site, by Income,
Price or Rent, Tenure, and Number of Bedrooms,
1974-83

(a)

Owners

| Income (price) Category | Number of Bedrooms | | | Total |
	2	3	4	
$ 4,000-$ 6,999				
(10,000 - 17,499)	79	131	84	294
7,000-9,999				
(17,500 - 24,999)	200	367	243	810
10,000-11,999				
(25,000 - 29,999)	120	208	131	459
12,000-14,000				
(30,000 - 37,499)	151	272	180	603
15,000-24,999				
(37,500 - 62,499)	152	275	185	612
25,000-49,999)				
(62,500 - 124,999)	57	92	55	204
50,000 and over				
(125,000 and over)	5	7	6	18
Total	764	1,352	884	3,000

Renters

| Income (rent) Category | Number of Bedrooms | | | | Total |
	0	1	2	3	
$ 4,000-$ 6,999					
(83 - 144)	24	87	126	136	373
7,000-9,999					
(145 - 207)	21	80	153	197	451
10,000-11,999					
(208 - 249)	10	43	82	102	237
12,000-14,999					
(250 - 311)	10	37	70	91	208
15,000-24,999					
(312 - 519)	10	37	70	89	206
25,000-49,999					
(520 - 1040)	2	4	9	10	25
50,000 and over					
(1,041 and over)	—	—	—	—	—
Total	77	288	510	625	1,500

TABLE 9.3

Site Household Characteristics, 1974-83

Population	Under 35	35-44	45-64	65 and over	Total
Persons per Household:					
1	23	45	194	158	420
2	171	149	935	477	1,732
3	238	197	324	9	768
4	278	306	194	—	778
5 or more	284	383	135	—	802
Total	994	1,080	1,782	644	4,500
Number of Children Under Eighteen Years:					
0	177	165	1,083	630	2,055
1	244	209	351	14	818
2	282	313	207	—	802
3	173	205	82	—	460
4 or more	118	188	59	—	365
Total	944	1,080	1,782	644	4,500
Number in Labor Force:					
0	77	9	53	223	362
1	537	661	813	178	2,189
2	310	353	691	70	1,424
3 or more	70	57	225	173	525
Total	994	1,080	1,782	644	4,500
Head Only in Labor Force	507	650	772	139	2,068
Share of Total	50.4	60.2	43.3	21.6	50.0
Head and Wife in Labor Force	280	331	627	45	1,283
Share of Total	28.2	30.6	35.2	7.0	28.5

TABLE 9.4

Summary Characteristics of the
Projected Households

Median Number of Persons by Number of Bedrooms	Units (mix)	Persons per Household	Total Population
Owner Occupied:			
2	764 (25.4)	3.18	2,429
3	1,352 (45.1)	3.30	4,462
4	884 (29.5)	3.51	3,099
All Owner Occupied	3,000 (100.0)	3.30	9,990
Renter Occupied:			
0	77 (5.1)	1.06	82
1	288 (19.2)	1.62	466
2	510 (34.0)	2.56	1,305
3	625 (41.7)	3.04	1,897
All Renter Occupied	1,500 (100.0)	2.50	3,750
Total	4,500	3.05	13,740

Note: Median income: owner occupied, $11,725; renter occupied, $9,507; all occupied, $10,925.

3. Multiunit low rise—densest of the three types and, along with the attached housing, is a form of clustered housing—a garden apartment.

A range of densities was considered for each dwelling-unit type; however, a single density was chosen for each for purposes of analysis, except for single-family detached, where more expensive units were planned at a lower density, two per acre. The densities chosen, as well as the tenure of each of the units, is shown below:

Type Dwelling Unit	Density (units per acre)	Tenure
Single-family detached (X,R)	2, 5	Owner
Single-family attached (S)	10	Renter
Multi-unit low rise (L)	20	Renter

TABLE 9.5

Projected Demand Schedule, 1974-83
(a)
Single-Family Dwelling Units

| Year | Single-Family Attached | | Single-Family Detached (five per acre) | | Single-Family Detached (two per acre) |
	2 Bedrooms[a]	3 Bedrooms[b]	3 Bedrooms[b]	4 Bedrooms[c]	4 Bedrooms[c]
1974			63	456	70
1975	242	406	16	140	35
1976	242	406	33	175	35
1977	242	406	13	140	35
1978	242	406	33	246	18
1979	484	812	29	211	18
1980	242	406	33	246	18
1981	484	812	29	211	35
1982	127	198	66	463	18
1983	127	228	66	463	70
Total	2,432	4,080	381	2,751	352

Low-Rise Units

Year	0 Bedrooms[d]	1 Bedroom[e]	2 Bedrooms[f]	3 Bedrooms[g]	Cum. Project, Population	Cumulative Project, Students
	1.06	1.62	2.56	3.04		
1974	15	92	261	386	1,343	298
1975	15	92	261	386	2,936	652
1976	7	48	130	182	4,194	931
1977	7	44	130	204	5,415	1,202
1978	7	44	130	191	6,732	1,495
1979	7	48	130	194	8,665	1,924
1980	7	44	130	119	9,910	2,200
1981	7	29	66	119	11,702	2,598
1982	7	24	64	119	12,788	2,839
1983					13,742	3,051
Total	79	465	1,302	1,900	13,742	

[a]People per dwelling unit equals 3.18.
[b]People per dwelling unit equals 3.30.
[c]People per dwelling unit equals 3.51.
[d]People per dwelling unit equals 1.06.
[e]People per dwelling unit equals 1.62.
[f]People per dwelling unit equals 2.56.
[g]People per dwelling unit equals 3.04.

It was necessary in determining the sale price of land for various uses to consider a preliminary sketch plan for the development. If the linear programming model had been used, estimates of the sale price of land would be made and the solution of the model would be the preliminary land use plan, capable of being translated into a sketch plan. This plan would be costed out to arrive at more appropriate sales prices. In the study estimates were made of land sale prices, and several iterations were made through the land value flow chart (Figure 5.2). Additional assumptions made during the course of the Highlands project were as follows:

1. The only land to be developed for sale would be residential, commercial, and industrial.

2. The costs of developing land for community facilities and recreation uses (twenty acres) were incurred by the developer, but were considered in a special account.

3. Land for educational use was assume to remain unimproved—fifteen acres would be dedicated to the school district in 1978 and fifteen acres for this purpose in 1982.

4. Land for commercial space was fixed at 8.6 acres and was scheduled for sale in 1974.

5. Industrial land was fixed at ten acres and scheduled for sale in 1976.

6. The land purchased by builders would not have on-site improvements; however, off-site improvements would be performed by the developer.

7. Land would be sold to builders in parcels (no on-site improvements), and no lead time for on-site improvements and construction was provided.

8. Unsold land was taxed as unimproved land at a rate of $190.569 per $1,000 assessed valuation—the combined county and town tax rate.

9. All dollars are constant 1970 dollars—no attempt was made to predict rising construction costs, inflation, rising incomes, and so forth.

10. One-half of the 1,760 acres would be purchased in 1972 and the remaining one-half in 1973.

11. From the 1,760 acres to be purchased, only 526.3 acres of the flatter uplands area would be developed for sale.

The land sale prices used in the last iteration are shown in Table 9.6. The land improvement costs per unit consists of the following: (a) the land acquisition costs—based on estimates of realtors and

recent acquisitions in the site area: (1) river bottom land, 130 acres
at $1,000 per acre; (2) slope land, 915 acres at $200 per acre; (3)
plateau land, 715 acres at $3,000 per acre—valued at $2.458 million;
(b) site improvement costs—computed from the sketch plan and presented in Table 9.7—total $3,252,500; (c) operating expenses—origi-
nally estimated from discussions with new community consultants—
estimated at $4,478,500, based upon previous iterations in calculating
land values. The total estimated development costs, which served
as input into the last iteration, was $10.189 million and was allocated
by type of use and acreage, resulting in an average cost per acre.
This figure was further refined for the residential portion of the
development into a cost per dwelling unit. The construction costs
per unit were estimated by the Highlands staff, with assistance from
personnel in the Center for Architectural Research at Rensselaer
Polytechnic Institute.

The use of the linear programming model can now be illustrated
by using as inputs the land sale prices, the demand schedule, saleable
land required for development, and the technical coefficients—people
per unit and units per acre. Five iterations of the linear programming model were necessary to arrive at a final plan for development.
In all cases the model was solved on an IBM computer model 360/50,
using IBM's MPS/360.

ITERATIONS OF THE LINEAR
PROGRAMMING MODEL

Iteration 1

The dimensions of this problem were 132 (constraints) x 132
(decision variables). An optimal solution was obtained after 131
iterations, taking 1.56 minutes. Instead of treating the land to be
allocated to commercial and industrial uses as fixed, they were
treated as bounded decision variables; i.e., the land to be allocated,
in acres, to commercial use in 1974 was given by

$$C_{1974} \leq Y^C_{1974} (523.6), \text{ and}$$

$$7.6 \leq C_{1974} \leq 9.6,$$

and the land to be allocated to industrial use in 1976 was

TABLE 9.6

Land Sale Prices Summary

(a)

Single-Family Detached

Costs and Value	5 per Acre 3 Bedrooms	5 per Acre 4 Bedrooms	2 per Acre 4 Bedrooms	Single-Family Attached 2 Bedrooms	3 Bedrooms
Construction Costs per Unit	$22,800	$30,000	$50,000	$14,400	$17,000
Land Improvement Costs per Unit	3,892	3,892	9,729	1,946	1,946
Market Value per Unit	26,692	33,892	59,729	16,346	18,946
Value of Land per Unit	5,338	6,778	11,946	3,269	3,789

(b)

Low-Rise Dwelling Units

Costs and Value	0 Bedrooms	1 Bedroom	2 Bedrooms	3 Bedrooms
Construction Costs per Unit	$10,400	$13,830	$16,410	$19,380
Land Improvement Costs per Unit	973	973	973	973
Market Value per Unit	11,373	14,803	17,383	20,353
Value of Land per Unit	2,275	2,961	3,477	4,071

(c)

Commercial, Retail, and Office

Cost and Value	The value of land for these uses was determined to be $0.50 per square foot

(d)

Industrial

Cost and Value	The value of land for this use was determined to be $0.25 per square foot

TABLE 9.7

Site Improvement Costs Summary, 1973, 1976, and 1979

Categories and Item Charges	Cost	1973	1976	1979
		(thousands of dollars)		
Roads:				
Parkway	$12.42 per square yard	$ 344.4		
Transit	3.31 per square yard	70.0		
Neighborhood roads	4.66 per square yard	17.6	$ 29.0	$ 159.5
Collector streets	4.66 per square yard	39.8	188.9	
Sidewalks	9.96 per square yard	29.2	39.0	136.3
Curbing	8.07 per lineal foot	53.2	71.0	248.6
Subtotal		554.2	327.9	544.4
Sewers:				
Main sewer	40.12 per lineal foot	280.8		
Collector sewers	7.95 per lineal foot	72.0	70.0	122.4
Subtotal		352.8	70.0	122.4
Utilities:				
Water	8.03 per lineal foot	72.8	70.7	123.7
Gas	4.38 per lineal foot	39.7	38.5	67.5
Electricity	5.00 per lineal foot	45.3	44.0	77.0
Lighting	3.71 per lineal foot	33.6	32.6	57.1
Subtotal		191.4	185.8	325.3
Storm Drainage	12.67 per lineal foot	114.8	111.5	195.1
Landscaping	0.06 per square foot	82.9	37.0	37.0
Grand Total		$1,296.1	$732.2	$1,224.2

Note: Acreage is as follows: 1973—thirty-six acres; 1976—fourteen acres; 1979—fourteen acres.

148

$$I_{1976} \leq Y^I_{1976} \ (523.6), \text{ and}$$

$$9.0 \leq I_{1976} \leq 11.0.$$

The land allocation constraints corresponding to each of these is the value taken on by C and I. The population constraints, land use constraints, and land allocation constraints are given by (6.1), (6.2), (6.12) abridged, and (6.13)—on pp. 116-118 in Chapter 6. The results of this trial were as follows: (a) the total saleable land required for development was validated to be 523.6 acres; (b) the maximum revenue obtainable given the imposed constraints was $19,952,147; and (c) the optimal land allocations were as follows:

Use	Optimal Land Allocation (acres)	
Single-family detached (2 units per acre)	50.14	(50)
Single-family detached (5 units per acre)	179.84	(180)
Single attached	200.11	(200)
Multi-unit low rise	74.76	(75)
Commercial	9.6	(8.6)
Industrial	9.14	(10)

Iteration 2

Based upon land allocations employed in the Highlands project, the problem was resolved using the values given in the parentheses above. However, the problem had no feasible solution. The constraints violated were the land allocation constraints for single-family detached (five units per acre) and multi-unit low rise. Two possibilities exist: (a) if the land can be reallocated, the current solution can be used to determine where and in what amount land can be reallocated; and (b) if the land cannot be reallocated, the current solution can be used to determine by how much land usage in the infeasible constraints must be decreased in order to become feasible.

Iteration 3

In this trial the land allocations in the infeasible constraints were decreased to 74.5 acres and 179.5 acres, and the difference— 1 acre—was added to the industrial land allocation, for a total of 11 acres. The dimensions of this problem were 132 (constraints) x 126 (decision variables). An optimal solution was obtained in 126 iterations, taking 3.73 minutes. The results of this trial were as follows: (a) a maximum revenue of $19,922,565 was obtained, resulting in a decrease of $28,582 from the first trial; and (b) optimal land allocations were obtained, from which parcelizations could heuristically be determined or validated.

Iteration 4

This trial assumed that land could not be reallocated. Therefore, land for the infeasible constraints were decreased to 74.5 acres and 179.5 acres, leaving a total of 522.6 saleable acres. All other land allocations were held constant (values in parentheses, p. 149). The result of decreasing the saleable acreage by a single acre led to a reduction in revenue of $10,980 from the revenue calculated, assuming that land could be reallocated. The price paid for inflexibility, therefore, was the revenue derivable from the sale of one acre of industrial land.

Iteration 5

Using the solution for trial 3 and the procedure discussed in Chapter 7, p. 130, all parcelizations chosen in the Highlands project, except for two, were found to be feasible. The parcels affected were those where the land allocations were originally infeasible. The timing of parcels was unchanged; however, the sizes were modified where required to maintain feasibility. In addition to the constraints already employed, parcelization constraints corresponding to (6.33) were added, and the problem was resolved. Parcelization constraints of the form of (6.23) were not required, since the developer did not perform the on-site improvements. The dimensions of this problem were 170 (rows) x 160 (decision variables). An optimal solution was obtained in 162 iterations, taking 2.18 minutes. The results of this trial are as follows: (a) the maximum revenue, (b) the optimal land use plan, (c) the optimal parcelization schedule, and (d) the optimal development schedule. The maximum revenue obtainable is $19,922,258. The optimal parcelization schedule and development schedule resulting from the constraints imposed on development in iteration 5 are presented in Tables 9.8 and 9.9, respectively. The figures in Table 9.9 have been rounded off; therefore, as in Chapter 4, they are theoretically not feasible, since the values of the decision variables from linear programming solution need not be integer.

Before the financial feasibility of the proposed plan for development can be evaluated, it is necessary to compare the computed land sale prices to the land sale prices used in obtaining the solution. It is first necessary in determining the land sale prices to translate the solution obtained from iteration 5 into a sketch plan containing enough information for costing. The solution obtained using LP was not significantly different from the final plan obtained and costed out in the Highlands project. Therefore, all costs are as previously reported, except for operating expenses. The actual operating expenses incurred are 30 percent of gross sales, or $6,122,158. Real estate taxes are, as before, $620,515. Since land acquisition and site improvement costs are unchanged, the total development cost is $12,453,-773, or $23,785 per acre. When this value is further refined to a per unit cost of improvements, it is found that the computed land sale prices per unit are equal to the old sale prices per unit—the measure of equality is whether the per unit improvement costs are less than, or equal to, the old per unit land sale prices.

Since the spatial development plan is valid for the land values used in determining the optimal development schedule, the next step is to evaluate the plan's financial feasibility. The results of this analysis are in Appendix 9.1, where the profit and loss statement, cash flow statement, and measures of performances are presented. Since the purpose of this chapter is to illustrate the use of the model and procedures previously discussed, the analysis was performed assuming 100 percent equity—this would imply the existence of a development entity with enough financial resources to use equity funds for land acquisition and site improvements. The internal rate of return for this example was found to be 13.38 percent and is above the probable minimum desired rate of 10 percent for real estate ventures.

During the course of the Highlands study, various plans for development were evaluated and found financially unacceptable. A new development plan was conceived in each case, and the tedious task of performing the calculations leading up to, and including, the financial analysis was repeated. The link analysis is an attempt to provide a more responsive reaction to this part of the development process. In Table 9.10 costs were allocated on the basis of land utilization, as discussed in Chapter 8. The same data were employed to allocate costs on a market value basis—a commonly employed allocation procedure—and the internal rate of return obtained was 14 percent.

The information needed for the link procedure is presented in Table 9.10, where the proportion of land used, revenue obtained, and costs allocated over all uses are presented for each year.

TABLE 9.8

Proposed Parcelization Schedule, 1974–83
(acres)

Year	Owners Detached Housing 2 per Acre	5 per Acre	Renters Attached Housing 10 per Acre	20 per Acre	Community Facilities	Schools	Commercial	Industrial
1974	10			15				
1975	10	30	20	15	5		8.6	
1976		30	20	15	2			11
1977	11		20		2			
1978		30	20	15		15		
1979			40					
1980	10	30	20	14.5	5			
1981			40		2			
1982		30	20		2	15		
1983	9	29.5						

TABLE 9.9

Proposed Development Schedule, by Type of Dwelling Units, 1974-83

| | Owner-Occupied Units | | | | | Renter-Occupied Units | | | |
| | Attached Housing | | Detached Housing | | | | | | |
Year	2 Bedrooms 10 Units per Acre	3 Bedrooms 10 Units per Acre	3 Bedrooms 5 Units per Acre	4 Bedrooms 5 Units per Acre	4 Bedrooms 2 Units per Acre	0 Bedrooms 20 Units per Acre	1 Bedrooms 20 Units per Acre	2 Bedrooms 20 Units per Acre	3 Bedrooms 20 Units per Acre
1974			19	130	20	14	57	102	127
1975	76	123	3	40	10	9	57	102	127
1976	76	123	10	50	10	7	30	51	60
1977	76	123	4	40	10	7	27	51	67
1978	76	123	10	70	5	7	27	51	63
1979	152	246	9	60	5	7	30	51	64
1980	76	123	10	70	5	7	27	51	39
1981	152	246	9	60	10	7	18	26	39
1982	40	60	20	132	5		15	25	39
1983	39	69	20	132	20				

TABLE 9.10

Case Study Data for Link Analysis

	PROPORTION OF AVAILABLE LAND USED FOR						PROPORTION OF TOTAL REVENUE FOR						PROPORTION OF COST ALLOCATED TO					
	X	R	S	L	CC	CI	X	R	S	L	CC	CI	X	R	S	L	CC	CI
1972	0.000	0.000	0.000	0.000	0.000	0.000	0.000	0.000	0.000	0.000	0.000	0.000	0.000	0.000	0.000	0.000	0.000	0.000
1973	0.000	0.000	0.000	0.000	0.000	0.000	0.000	0.000	0.000	0.000	0.000	0.000	0.000	0.000	0.000	0.000	0.000	0.000
1974	0.019	0.057	0.000	0.029	0.016	0.000	0.012	0.049	0.000	0.054	0.009	0.000	0.019	0.006	0.000	0.013	0.022	0.000
1975	0.010	0.016	0.038	0.028	0.000	0.000	0.006	0.014	0.036	0.053	0.000	0.000	0.038	0.022	0.010	0.013	0.000	0.000
1976	0.010	0.023	0.038	0.014	0.000	0.021	0.006	0.020	0.036	0.026	0.000	0.006	0.038	0.016	0.010	0.026	0.000	0.017
1977	0.010	0.017	0.038	0.014	0.000	0.000	0.006	0.015	0.036	0.027	0.000	0.000	0.038	0.022	0.010	0.025	0.000	0.000
1978	0.005	0.031	0.038	0.014	0.000	0.000	0.003	0.027	0.036	0.026	0.000	0.000	0.074	0.012	0.010	0.026	0.000	0.000
1979	0.005	0.026	0.076	0.014	0.000	0.000	0.003	0.023	0.072	0.027	0.000	0.000	0.074	0.014	0.005	0.025	0.000	0.000
1980	0.005	0.031	0.038	0.012	0.000	0.000	0.003	0.027	0.036	0.022	0.000	0.000	0.074	0.012	0.010	0.031	0.000	0.000
1981	0.010	0.026	0.076	0.009	0.000	0.000	0.006	0.023	0.072	0.016	0.000	0.000	0.038	0.014	0.005	0.043	0.000	0.000
1982	0.005	0.058	0.019	0.008	0.000	0.000	0.003	0.050	0.018	0.015	0.000	0.000	0.078	0.006	0.019	0.044	0.000	0.000
1983	0.019	0.058	0.021	0.000	0.000	0.000	0.012	0.050	0.020	0.000	0.000	0.000	0.019	0.006	0.018	0.000	0.000	0.000

TOTAL COST = 5710000 DUAL VARIABLE = 32690 TOTAL REVENUE = 19922528

X DENOTES SINGLE FAMILY DETACHED DWELLING UNITS AT A DENSITY OF 2/ACRE

R DENOTES SINGLE FAMILY DETACHED DWELLING UNITS AT A DENSITY OF 5/ACRE

S DENOTES SINGLE FAMILY ATTACHED DWEELLINGS AT A DENSITY OF 10/ACRE

L DENOTES LOW RISE APARTMENTS AT A DENSITY OF 20/ACRE

CC DENOTES COMMERCIAL SPACE IN ACRES

CI DENOTES INDUSTRIAL SPACE IN ACRES

APPENDIX 9.1

Financial Analysis for Case Study*

APPENDIX TABLE 9.1.1

SALES AND INCOME SUMMARY - NC BCRRCWIINGS

	LAND REVENUE + INTERIM INCOME	ABSORBED COST	PROPERTY TAXES	OPERATING EXPENSES	PROFIT/LOSS BEFORE INC TAX	PROVISION FOR TAXES	NET INCOME AFTER TAXES	CUMULATIVE NET INCOME
1972	$ 0	$ 0	$ 44499	$ 66000	$ -110499	$ -55249	$ -55250	$ -55250
1973	$ 0	$ 0	$ 85089	$ 80000	$ -165089	$ -82544	$ -82545	$ -137795
1974	$ 2479763	$ 342000	$ 78093	$ 743928	$ 1315742	$ 657871	$ 657871	$ 520076
1975	$ 2181138	$ 470000	$ 72238	$ 654341	$ 984559	$ 492279	$ 492280	$ 1012356
1976	$ 1868204	$ 606000	$ 64711	$ 560461	$ 637032	$ 318516	$ 318516	$ 1330872
1977	$ 1670626	$ 537000	$ 60040	$ 501187	$ 572399	$ 286199	$ 286200	$ 1617072
1978	$ 1832402	$ 691000	$ 53403	$ 549720	$ 538279	$ 269139	$ 269140	$ 1886212
1979	$ 2484609	$ 672000	$ 44420	$ 745382	$ 1022807	$ 511403	$ 511404	$ 2397616
1980	$ 1735984	$ 719000	$ 39466	$ 520795	$ 456723	$ 228361	$ 228362	$ 2625978
1981	$ 2320377	$ 564000	$ 32395	$ 696113	$ 1027869	$ 513934	$ 513935	$ 3139913
1982	$ 1721762	$ 843000	$ 25421	$ 516528	$ 336813	$ 168406	$ 168407	$ 3308320
1983	$ 1627678	$ 243000	$ 19740	$ 488303	$ 876635	$ 438317	$ 438318	$ 3746638

*This analysis was conducted assuming 100 percent equity—no borrowing—and includes a profit-and-loss statement, a cash-flow statement, and measures of performance.

155

CASH FLOW PROJECTION – NO BORROWING

Year	LAND REVENUE + INTERIM INCOME	LAND + INVEST	IMPROVEMENT COSTS	WORKING CAPITAL	CHANGE IN WRKNG CAPTL	OPERATING EXPENSES	PROPERTY AND INCOME TAXES	CASH FLOW	CUMULATIVE CASH FLOW
1972	$ 0	$1229000	$ 0			$ 66000	$ -10750	$ -1284250	$ -1284250
1973	$ 0	$1229000	$1296000			$ 80000	$ 2545	$ -2607545	$ -3891795
1974	$ 2479763	$ 0	$ 0			$ 743928	$ 735964	$ 999871	$ -2891924
1975	$ 2181138	$ 0	$ 0			$ 654341	$ 564517	$ 962280	$ -1929544
1976	$ 1868204	$ 0	$ 732000			$ 560461	$ 383227	$ 192516	$ -1731128
1977	$ 1670626	$ 0	$ 0			$ 501187	$ 346239	$ 823200	$ -913928
1978	$ 1832402	$ 0	$ 0			$ 549720	$ 322542	$ 960140	$ 45212
1979	$ 2484609	$ 0	$1224000			$ 745382	$ 555823	$ -40596	$ 5516
1980	$ 1735984	$ 0	$ 0			$ 520795	$ 267827	$ 947362	$ 952978
1981	$ 2320377	$ 0	$ 0			$ 696113	$ 546329	$ 1077935	$ 2030913
1982	$ 1721762	$ 0	$ 0			$ 516528	$ 193827	$ 1011407	$ 3042320
1983	$ 1627678	$ 0	$ 0			$ 488303	$ 458057	$ 681318	$ 3723638

Source: U. S. Department of Housing and Development, New Communities: A Bibliography (Washington, D. C., 1969).

APPENDIX TABLE 9.1.3

MEASURES OF PERFORMANCE

	DISCOUNTED RATE OF RETURN NO BORROWINGS BORROWINGS	PAYBACK PERIOD (YEARS) NO BORROWINGS BORROWINGS	AVERAGE RATE OF RETURN NO BORROWINGS BORROWINGS
1972	*****		
1973	*****		
1974	*****		
1975	*****		
1976	*****		
1977	*****		
1978	C.37		
1979	C.C5		
1980	5.75		
1981	9.70		
1982	12.17		
1983	13.38		

***** DENOTES A NEGATIVE INTERNAL RATE OF RETURN

Referring to Table 9.10 the land made available in the Highlands study for single-family dwelling units at a density of two per acre is interpreted as being inefficiently utilized in 1978 (comparisons indicated by circled values in table) and could be more efficiently utilized if the land could be made available for multi-unit low-rise apartments at a density of twenty per acre in 1981 (comparisons indicated by blocked values in the table). It was stated in Chapter 8 that the purpose of the link procedure was to assist in arriving at logical changes in the current development plan. The result that land to be sold for building twenty dwelling units per acre is more valuable to the developer than land on which two dwelling units per acre are to be built is so obvious that it should not require any type of analysis—consider the development costs associated with each. Due to the complexity of the land development process and the lack of the link procedure, this result was not capitalized on in the various changes made to the development plan during the course of the Highlands project.

10

EXTENSIONS TO
THE CASE STUDY

The most critical component of a development plan is the demand schedule. A multitude of assumptions are used to derive a development schedule for a site from the market analysis for the region. The land absorbed during the development process is the source of revenue; however, it is directly related to the development schedule through assumptions on densities, family sizes, and so forth. Therefore, it is desirable to measure the sensitivity of the projected revenues to changes in the absorption of dwelling units. Conversely, it is also desirable to measure how sensitive the development plan is to changes in the revenues from the sale of various dwelling units.

The solution presented in Chapter 9, rather than being the "answer," represents the beginning of the analysis. Computational procedures are available that permit analysis of the solution and provide information on the sensitivity of the development schedule and concomitant revenues to changes in the assumptions. The mathematical programming system/360 procedures [41] contain, in addition to many other features, two postoptimality procedures that are of particular interest, the "range" and "parametric programming."

RANGE

Range provides information on all right-hand side values and decision variables. Of particular interests are the objective function coefficients (unit sale prices) and the right-hand side values corresponding to the demand schedule for the current optimal solution. The procedure computes, for the latter, how much each right-hand side value can be changed while all other right-hand side values are held constant, before the optimal basis will change. The range for the objective coefficients are similarly computed. Both of these ranges provide a measure of the sensitivity of the current solution to changes in assumptions on the projected market forecasts and the unit sale prices.

The Current Solution

The best possible plan (iteration 1) from the five iterations conducted and previously presented was relatively insensitive to changes in either the projected market demand or the unit sale prices. For example, the projection made for single-family detached units with four bedrooms at a density of five per acre in 1974 was 456 people. The range over which this plan (basis) would remain unchanged was 423 to 458 people. For each person below 456 not absorbed, a loss in revenue of $1,310 per person would result. A similar increase in revenue would result for each person over 456 that is absorbed. This unit sales revenue is only valid for the stipulated range. For this very same dwelling unit, the sale price of land per unit was determined to be $6,778 per unit. But, the range over which this sale price could vary without causing a change in the basis is $4,600 per unit to infinity. Since $6,778 per unit for a four-bedroom single-family detached at a density of five per acre is considered by some to be rather high for this type of unit in the area of the site, it is informative to know that a reduction in the sale price could be made originally to motivate sales if this represented the plan for development, noting a loss in revenue would result.

The land allocation constraints (iteration 3) are the most binding. As a result of their introduction, the lower bounds on the demand schedule and unit sales price were increased. The introduction of the parcelization constraints (iteration 5) led to a decrease in the upper bounds on the demand schedule, without an associated affect on the lower bounds; therefore, the affect on the range resulting from constraining the problem will be illustrated, using the results of iteration 5. The range on the demand for the same dwelling unit as above, for which the basis remained unchanged, was 450 to 459 people at corresponding decreases and increases per person in revenue of $410. The upper bound on the sales price was still nonexistent, but the lower bound increased to $5,338 per unit. Although there is little latitude with respect to projected market demand, there is greater latitude with respect to changes in the sale price.

PARAMETRIC PROGRAMMING

Parametric analysis is an extension of the range procedure. Although the range procedure provides insight into the current solution, it does not address itself to the question of what happens to the optimal basis if two or more coefficients or right-hand side values simultaneously vary over some specified interval. The range procedure is typically conducted at the same time as the linear programming procedure is performed. The parametric analysis, on the other hand, is performed for specific questions asked, based on the current solution. Although procedures exist for conducting parametric analyses, not all postoptimality analysis are directly concerned with solution sensitivity. For example, if sufficient provision had not been made for moderate-income and elderly families in the current solution (iteration 5), then it would be necessary to modify the demand schedule to assure adequate provision, and the problem would be resolved.

A Governmental Request

Let us assume for this illustration that a sponsoring government agency has reviewed the proposed plan for development and concludes that the provision for housing for the elderly and moderate-income families with three to four children is inadequate. In order for the developer to receive the support provided by this agency, it will be necessary for him to include approximately 36 percent more elderly in zero- and one-bedroom low-rise units and 36 percent more moderate-income families in three-bedroom attached dwelling units than exist in his current plan for development. The questions confronting the developer are the following: (a) does such a guaranteed market exist, and (b) what will be the effect on his total revenue and plan for development as a result of this change?

The Moderate-Income and Elderly Market

Both the attached and low-rise units are renter occupied. Assume for the purposes of illustration that the sale price of land for the rental units is such that the units are rented at levels in accordance with the appropriate federal housing programs [24,39]. One such program is section 202 (housing for the elderly) of the Housing and Developing Act of 1969 which stipulates, in part, that the sponsor of such housing must be a nonprofit organization and that the income limits are dependent on the number of people in the family, but must be no greater than $6,600 or less than $4,500. Another program is section 236, rental and cooperative housing for low-moderate-income families. Among the stipulations are the following: (a) sponsors may be a nonprofit, limited dividend, or cooperative corporation; and

(b) income limits must be between $8,000 and $9,000. Since these figures are based on a study in Connecticut, a $7,000 maximum income limit will be used in this example.

In the regional forecast 46 percent, or 13,320 renter households (Table 9.1), may be considered to be composed of moderate-income and elderly families. The capture rates that were employed for the county and site were 35 percent and 30 percent, respectively. The total market of elderly and moderate-income families that is possible for the site is, therefore, 1,399 households. Of the renters currently planned for the site (Table 9.2), 25 percent are in this group (373 households), resulting in an untouched market of 1,026 such households. The additional requirements will be satisfied if provision is made for 7 additional zero-bedroom low-rise units, 26 one-bedroom low-rise units, and 114 three-bedroom single-family attached units—which, in aggregate, does not exceed the untouched market. The population involved is obtained by multiplying each of these dwelling units by the appropriate household size (people per unit), yielding 7, 42, and 376 people, respectively.

Affect on Revenue and Plan

A question that must be addressed is the timing of the housing. There are many ramifications to this question. If, for example, moderate-income housing is planned early in the development process, the market projected for the more affluent members of society may never be realized. Alternatively, if the developer waits too long in the development process, the community will have established itself as a middle-upper-class social group whose members may not want him to fulfill the governmental requirement. It has been assumed for illustrative purposes that housing for these additional people will be provided in equal amounts over the last six years of the project.

The procedure employed was to add one-sixth of the total additional housing requirement to the projected demand (current) for the last six years and to convert these demand schedule constraints to equalities, keeping all other constraints unchanged. This problem was resolved, yielding a total revenue of $19,998,651, $76,087 more than was realized in the former development plan. The higher revenue seems like a contradiction, but the developer, acting rationally, satisfies the guaranteed market and then sells to the remaining maximum revenue sources—constrained only by the market.

Sensitivity of Current Solution to
Revenue Changes

Provision was made in the current plan (iteration 5) for four-bedroom single-family detached units at a density of five per acre; however, it was felt by local realtors that this density was not at all common in the region. Confounding this problem was the knowledge that the swelling units in question would cost $33,892. It was felt desirable to test the affect on the plan for development if it became necessary to reduce the unit revenue for land sales in order that the dwelling units could be sold at a reduced price. Analyzing the range would provide insights into this possibility. If this occurred the developer would attempt to reduce his losses by increasing the unit sale price of land for single-family detached at a density of two per acre, a higher-priced unit.

The effect of these changes can be studied by performing a parametric analysis on the objective function. The procedure is to replace the original objective with the original objective, plus a multiple of a "change row," i.e., revenue = revenue + Δ change row. The function of this analysis is to generate a series of solutions as Δ is varied from zero to a maximum defined by the user. As Δ increases the solution is kept optimal and feasible for the current value of Δ, by changing the basis when necessary. For this problem Δ was incremented by $678 per unit for each problem until a defined maximum of $2,034 per unit was reached. The change row was defined such that for each solution the unit revenues for single-family detached (five per acre) were decreased by $678 per unit, while, concurrently, the unit revenues for single-family detached (two per acre) were increased by $1,356 per unit. This parametric analysis involved four solutions corresponding to each value taken on by Δ ; the results of parametric analysis on objective function are summarized below:

Δ Value	Total Revenue	Solution
0	$19,922,564	Current solution (iteration 5)
678	19,526,774	Solution (basis) unchanged
1356	19,130,985	Solution (basis) unchanged
1440	—	Basis changed; with this basis change Δ can be increased indefinitely without requiring another basis change to maintain optimality

Δ Value	Total Revenue	Solution
2034	18,736,214	Current solution has a new basis, but the only difference that resulted was one less dwelling unit with four bedrooms (five per acre) built in 1974 and one more dwelling unit with three bedrooms (five per acre) built in 1975.

This analysis has revealed that the development schedule is insensitive to per unit changes in revenue for the two types of dwelling units being considered.

11

SUMMARY AND CONCLUSIONS

In a recent article in <u>Fortune</u> [9], it was reported that the new communities that have received HUD-guaranteed assistance are serving as laboratories for testing various kinds of innovations. It was also noted that in the 1970's there will be an increase in the number of new communities throughout the United States. The success of these communities will depend upon the research activities currently underway as part of the New Community Program at HUD, as well as the efforts of independent researchers. The need for research on many topics—the relation of the new community to the surrounding environment, social and ecological factors, site location, financial matters, and so forth—is being addressed by the activities being undertaken at leading educational institutions—Cornell University, Syracuse University, North Carolina State University, Rensselaer Polytechnic Institute, and so forth—and the support being provided by public institutions, such as HUD and the Urban Development Corporation of New York State.

The research reported on here is unique, since other approaches to financing deal only with financial feasibility—characterized by rate of return models that allow the development entity to calculate, for various assumptions of financing costs, its return on investment. Our approach deals explicitly with the interrelationships among market, fiscal, and financial feasibility. In the advent of financial infeasibility, a method is proposed that links the financial analysis to the current plan for development.

This research has not dealt with financial planning models, which optimally determine sources, amounts, and timing of financing needs. However, this research has described the development process—thereby

165

identifying the sources and uses of funds, the lack of synchronization
of cash inflows and outflows, and the amount and timing of financing
needs. To optimally determine a method of financing, it remains
to identify the sources of financing that are employable in the new
community development process [6,8,21,25,30,37,52]. It must be noted,
however, that the sources of funds being employed in new community
developments are many and varied. In a recent article Harold S.
Jensen [33] describes the changes that have occurred and are expected
to occur in the world of real estate finance, whereas in a second
article, William R. Beaton [7] describes the types of "creative
financing" that are currently being used. Until the sources of financing
for real estate become stabilized, it is difficult to visualize any
practitioner attempting to determine an optimal method of financing
for new community developments in the sense that Y. E. Orgler [47,48]
has dealt with the cash management problem for industrial corporations.
Other works that deal with financing are those of A. Charnes, W. W.
Cooper, and M. H. Miller [11], Y. Ijiri, F. K. Levy, and R. C. Lyon [31],
Charnes, Cooper, and Ijiri, [10], H. M. Weingartner [63], and A. A.
Robichek, D. Teichroew, and J. M. Jones [53].

Our research activities have illustrated the usefullness of
linear programming as an aid to developers in the land development
process. The appropriateness of the linear programming model in
the land development process is exemplified by the fact that (a) interrelationships characterizing a new community can be explicitly
expressed and dealt with; (b) social constraints can be identified, and
the development schedule that maximizes revenue can be determined;
and (c) the link between the financial analysis and the development
schedule is a pragmatic one and should be of value to developers.

SUGGESTIONS FOR FURTHER STUDY

This work has resulted in a methodology to assist the developer
of large-scale land developments. The use of linear programming
requires that the variables be continuous; this is not restrictive, since
mixed-integer packages are available, in particular, an extension of
the MPS/360 procedures [42]. The only integer decision variables
in the formulation are those defining the number of dwelling units by
size and tenure. The merit of converting the LP model into a mixed-
integer multi-period linear programming model would have to be
weighed against the computational efficiency of the algorithm employed.

The problem presented in Chapter 9 was solved using the MPS/
360 procedures, with the results serving as input to the financial
analysis. This analysis was performed in a separate operation. It
would be more useful to the developer to have the essential features

of the simulation model used to generate the output in Appendix 5.1 combined with the mathematical programming approach.

The multi-period LP model was applied to a land development project, as discussed in Chapter 9. However, this methodology should be further evaluated by working closely with consultants and a development staff in planning a development program from inception. With the advent of the new ALPHA system for IBM's 360 or 370 systems, Fortran IV can be used as a means of communication on time sharing systems; the MPS/360 will be available for use on time sharing. This capability will facilitate the use of the LP model as an integral part of the development process, permitting the system analyst to participate as an effective member of the development team.

An analytical representation that would be of assistance to developers, public officials, and so forth would deal with elements of the market analysis—income distribution, age, and so forth—and would yield an explicit demand schedule. A model that deals simultaneously with income, family size, age of head of household, and so forth is J. P. Crecine's time oriented metropolitan model (TOMM) [12]. A second model that considers the same is the community model simulator (CMS), employed by Decision Sciences Corporation in their PROMUS (provincial municipal simulator) simulation effort for the city of Toronto, Canada [50]. A programmed modification of one or both of these may yield the desired result—a projected demand schedule. This model could then be linked to the LP model described herein.

More direct approaches to analyzing the financial feasibility of the development plan are needed. Currently, the discounted internal rate of return (IRR) is used as the indicator of the financial feasibility of a development plan. Another approach is to have the developer specify a desirable IRR (or, at least, a lower bound). The developer would therefore seek to minimize the divergence between the actual IRR and the target IRR subject to the environmental constraints (land use, demand, allocation, parcelization, and so forth) in arriving at a plan for development. Such a problem formulation may be amenable to solution, using goal programming [38,10].

It was shown that, due to the dependence of costs on the spatial location of parcels, it was prohibitive to optimally determine parcel sizes and timing. If the linearity assumption between parcel size and cost is not an unrealistic one, the possible locations for each parcel by type can be identified and the per unit cost determined. The revenue objective can then be used to optimally determine a development schedule and land allocations; whereupon, either LP or mixed integer programming would be employed to optimally select those parcel sizes by use and timing that minimizes the development

cost, subject to the land allocation and development schedule constraints.

The link analysis was developed for purposes of analysis. It
was shown for the example considered in Chapter 9 that the affect on
the internal rate of return of allocating cost to sales using the market
value basis and the dual evaluators differed little. It was not the
purpose of this thesis to explore cost-accounting schemes for purposes
of reporting income; therefore, the merit of this approach as a tool
for managerial accounting requires further investigation.

REFERENCES

1. Advisory Commission on Intergovernmental Relations, Urban and Rural America: Policies for Future Growth, (U. S. Government Printing Office, Washington, D. C., 1968), p. 61.

2. Ibid., p. 156.

3. Alfred, A. M., and J. B. Evans. Discounted Cash Flow, (Chapman and Hall, Ltd., London, 1969), pp. 3-10.

4. Alonso, W. "The Mirage of New Towns," The Public Interest (Spring 1970), p. 16.

5. Ibid., p. 10.

6. Apgar IV, Mahlon. "New Business from New Towns," Harvard Business Review, XLV, I (January-February 1971), pp. 90-109.

7. Beaton, William R. "Creative Financing of Real Estate," Urban Land, XXX, 6 (June 1971), pp. 11-16.

8. Belser, J. "On Financing New Communities Through a Public-Private Partnership," (December 1969). Unpublished.

9. Carruth, E. "The Big Move to New Towns," Fortune (September 1971), pp. 94-97 and 147-51.

10. Charnes, A., W. W., Cooper, and Y. Ijiri. "Breakeven Budgeting and Programming to Goals," Journal of Accounting Research, I, 1 (Spring 1963), pp. 16-43.

11. _____, _____, and M. H. Miller. "Application of Linear Programming to Financial Budgeting and the Costing of Funds," Journal of Business, XXXII, I (January 1959), pp. 20-46.

12. Crecine, J. P. "Spatial Location Decisions and Urban Structure: A Time-Oriented Model," (Institute of Public Policy Studies, Discussion Paper No. 4. Ann Arbor: University of Michigan, March 1969).

13. Dienstfrey, T. "A Note on the Economics of Community Building," Journal of the American Institute of American Planners, XXXIII (March 1967), pp. 120-23.

14. Eichler, Edward P., and Marshall Kaplan, The Community Builders, (Berkeley and Los Angeles: University of California Press, 1967), p. x.

15. Ibid., pp. 54-79.

16. Ibid., p. 182.

17. Ibid., pp. 187-96.

18. Gans, Herbert J. The Levittowners: Ways of Life and Politics in a New Suburban Community. (New York: Pantheon Books, 1967).

19. General Electric Company, Financial Analysis Model, 1969.

20. Glazer, Nathan. Testimony before the National Commission on Urban Problems, Vol. II, p. 246. Reported by Morton J. Schussheim "Housing in Perspective," in The Public Interest (Spring 1970), p. 25.

21. Gliege, J. G., "New Towns: Policy Problems in Regulating Development," Papers in Public Administration No. 17 (Tempe: Institute of Public Administration, Arizona State University, 1970).

22. Ibid., p. 22.

23. Goodschalk, David R., "Comparative New Community Design, Journal of the American Institute of Planners, XXXIII (November 1967), p. 382.

24. Governmental Housing Programs for Low and Moderate Income Families: A Summary (Washington, D. C.: Non Profit Housing Center, March 1971).

25. Hayes, S. L., III, and L. M. Harlan, "Real Estate as a Corporate Investment," Harvard Business Review, XLV, 4 (July-August 1967), pp. 144-60.

26. Hoppenfeld, Morton, "A Sketch of the Planning-Building Process for Columbia, Maryland," Journal of the American Institute of Planners, XXXIII (November 1967), p. 399.

27. Howard, Ebenezer, Garden Cities of To-Morrow (London: Faber and Faber, 1945), p. 106.

28. Ibid., p. 26.

29. Ibid., pp. 104-6.

30. Howes, J. B., "The Shape of Federal Involvement in New Community Development," Paper presented at the New Towns Seminar-Series III, Center for Urban and Regional Studies, Institute for Research in Social Sciences, University of North Carolina, 1970.

31. Ijiri, Y., F. K. Levy, and R. C. Lyon. "A Linear Programming Model for Budgeting and Financial Planning," Journal of Accounting Research, I, 2 (Autumn 1963), pp. 198-212.

32. Israel Institute of Urban Studies, "Town Planning and Welfare Maximization: A Methodological Approach," (Tel-Aviv, 1968). Unpublished.

33. Jensen, Harold S., "The Changing World of Real Estate Finance," Urban Land, XXX, 6 (June 1971), pp. 3-10.

34. Jones, G. M., "Some Problems in Accounting for Land Development," Management Accounting (August 1968), pp. 27-33.

35. Kelly, K. R., "A Net Cash Flow—Internal Rate of Return Computer Model for Real Estate Investment Analysis." Unpublished master's thesis, School of Business Administration, University of California, 1969.

36. Lindbloom, Charles, "The Science of Muddling Through," Public Administration Review, XIX, 2 (1959), p. 80.

37. Litchfield, Nathaniel, Economics of Planned Development, (London: Estates Gazette, 1956).

38. Mao, J. C. T., Quantitative Analysis of Financial Decisions, (London: Macmillan Company, 1969).

39. Marcuse, Peter, "Comparative Analysis of Federally-Aided Low- and Moderate-Income Housing Programs," reprinted from Journal of Housing, XXVI, 10 (November 1969).

40. Marshall Valuation Service, (New York: Marshall and Swift Publication Company, 1970-71).

41. Mathematical Programming System/360 (360A-CO-14X), Application Description (H20-0290-3). (White Plains, N.Y.: International Business Machines Corporation, 1967).

42. Mathematical Programming System Extended (MPSX) Mixed Integer Programming (5734-XM4). (White Plains, N.Y.: International Business Machines Corporation, 1971).

43. McKeever, J. R., ed., The Community Builders Handbook, (Washington, D. C.: Urban Land Institute, 1968).

44. National Committee on Urban Growth Policy, The New City, (New York: Praeger Publishers, 1969).

45. U. S. Department of Housing and Development, New Communities A Bibliography, (Washington, D. C., 1969).

46. New Communities: Systems For Planning and Evaluation, (Jenkintown, Pa.: Decision Sciences Corporation, 1971).

47. Orgler, Y. E., "An Unequal-Period Model for Cash Management Decisions," Management Science, XVI, 2 (October 1969), pp. B-77—B-92.

48. _____, Cash Management: Methods and Models (Belmont, Calif.: Wadsworth Publishing Company, 1970).

49. Osborn, Frederick J., Genesis of Welwyn Garden City, Some Jubilee Memoirs, Edited and with a foreword by Baroness Sharpor Hornsey (London: Town and Country Planning Association, 1919), p. 26.

50. PROMUS, (Jenkintown, Pa.: Decision Sciences Corporation, May 1970).

51. Ricks, R. B., "A Tool for Managerial Analysis in Land Development," Journal of the American Institute of American Planners, XXXIII (March 1967), pp. 117-20.

52. _____, "Real Estate Development Financing," California Management Review (Spring 1968), pp. 81-89.

53. Robichek, A. A., D. Teichroew and J. M. Jones, "Optimal Short Term Financing Decision," Management Science, XII, 1 (September 1965), pp. 1-36.

54. Schussheim, M. J., "Housing in Perspective," The Public Interest (Spring 1970), pp. 18-30.

55. Stone, P. A., Housing, Town Development, Land and Cost (London: Estates Gazette, 1964).

56. _____, "Decision Techniques for Town Development," Operations Research Quarterly, XV, 3 (1964), pp. 185-205.

57. The American City Corporation and the Rouse Company, "An Analysis of Development Trends and Projections and Recommendations for a New City in South Richmond," (Columbia, Md.: The Rouse Company, May 1970).

58. "The Highlands Project: A Development/Conservation Plan for a New Community in the Capital District of New York State." Troy, N.Y: Rensselaer Polytechnic Institute, June 1971.

59. The National Commission on Urban Problems, Alternatives to Urban Sprawl: Legal Guidelines for Government Action, Research Report No. 15 (Washington, D. C., U. S. Government Printing Office, 1968), p. 5.

60. "The Story of a Market Success—and a Financial Failure," House and Home, XXXII, 2 (August 1967), p. 56.

61. Thorne, O. J., "Cash Flow Analysis and Investment Strategy for Industrial Park Development," Society of Industrial Realtors-Newsletter (April-May 1971), pp. 3-9.

62. Von Hertzen, H., and P. Spreiregan, Building a New Town: Findland's New Garden City: Tapiola Cambridge: Massachusetts Institute of Technology Press, 1971).

63. Weingartner, H. M., Mathematical Programming and the Analysis of Capital Budgeting Problems (Englewood Cliffs, N.J.: Prentice-Hall, 1963).

64. Welsh, James, "Tapiola a Model Venture," Evening Star (Washington, D. C.), February 4, 1969.

65. Wendt, Paul F., "Large-Scale Community Development," Journal of Finance (May 1967), pp. 220-39.

66. _____, and A. R. Cerf. Real Estate Investment Analysis and Taxation (New York: McGraw Hill, 1969).

67. Winston, Oliver C., "An Urbanization Pattern for the United States: Some Considerations for the Decentralization of Excellence," reprinted in Congressional Record, October 10, 1967, p. S14506-7. Reported in Urban and Rural America, p. 56.

68. Wren, Kenneth, "Financial Appraisal of a New City," (Buckinghamshire, England, Milton Keynes Development Corporation, March 1970). Unpublished.

RICHARD L. HEROUX is Senior Operations Research Analyst of Associates Corporation of North America, South Bend, Indiana. He received a B.S. in chemical engineering from Clarkson College of Technology and holds an M.S. in management and a Ph.D. in operations research and statistics from Rensselaer Polytechnic Institute. Dr. Heroux has conducted research in the areas of financial analysis as pertained to the development of new communities. His current work involves internal consulting and support of finance operations planning.

WILLIAM A. WALLACE is Associate Professor of Management and Director, Program in Public Management, Rensselaer Polytechnic Institute. He received a B.Ch.E. in chemical engineering from Illinois Institute of Technology and holds an M.S. in management and a Ph.D. in operations research and statistics from Rensselaer Polytechnic Institute.

Professor Wallace has published in the areas of mineral resources, planning in higher education, and law enforcement in such journals as Society of Mining Engineers: Transactions, Socio-Economic Planning Sciences, and Management Science.

His current research interests include mineral resource planning and higher education, as well as continued work in planning for new communities. He is a member of TIMS, ORSA, and Sigma Xi.